FEL
STORIES

FELT BOARD STORIES

WRITTEN BY
LIZ & DICK WILMES

ART BY
JANET McDONNELL

A **BUILDING BLOCKS** PUBLICATION

38W567 BRINDLEWOOD, ELGIN, ILLINOIS 60123

Cover and Text Illustrations: Janet McDonnell
    Arlington Heights, Illinois

Cover Design: David Van Delinder
    Studio IVV, Elgin, Illinois

Text and Graphics Layout: Karen Wollscheid
    McHenry, Illinois

Disclaimer
The publisher and the authors cannot be held responsible for injury, mishap, or damages incurred during the use of or because of the activities in this book. The authors recommend appropriate and reasonable supervision at all times based on the age and capability of each child.

PUBLISHED BY:

38W567 Brindlewood
Elgin, Illinois 60123

DISTRIBUTED BY:

Gryphon House
P.O. Box 207
Beltsville, MD 20704
(Educational Stores & Catalogs)

Consortium Book Sales
1045 Westgate Drive
St. Paul, MN 55114
(U.S. Book Trade)

Monarch Books
5000 Dufferin St., Unit K
Downsview, Ontario
Canada M3H 5T5
(All Canadian Orders)

CONTENTS

CONTENTS

SPRING

SUMMER

LITERACY

FELT BOARD STORIES
naturally encourages
children to get actively
involved in each story.

Enjoy them with your
children.

INTRODUCTION

BEFORE READING/TELLING EACH STORY

1. Introduce the children to the story and the characters.

2. Tell the children how they will be involved in the story as you read/tell it.

- Guess riddles.
- Sing.
- Add their own thoughts.
- Count.
- Clap.
- Chant along.
- And so much more!

WHILE READING/TELLING EACH STORY

Encourage your children to participate in the natural storyline by counting, singing, clapping, guessing riddles, etc.

In Addition You Can Have Children:

1. Chant repetitive lines and sentences.

2. Pretend they are different characters.

3. Answer questions about the story.

4. Predict what is going to happen to different characters.

5. Think of different ways the story could end.

6. Put the felt pieces on the board.

AFTER READING / TELLING EACH STORY

Talk About the Story – Children Could:

1. Retell the story.

2. Create new endings.

3. Discuss each story.

   - Have your children experienced any of the same situations or adventures as the characters in the story? Let them relate their stories.

   - Who was their favorite character and why?

   - How did different characters make them feel?

   - Were any of the characters like people or animals they know? Who? What?

PLAY STORY GAMES (Described After Each Story)

These Games Will Help Children:

- Enjoy the stories even more.

- Expand their knowledge of the characters, story lines, and settings.

- Relate the stories to their own lives and families.

Make STORY FOLDERS and FELT PIECES

Story Folders

1. Duplicate each page of the story.

2. Glue the story pages into a colored file folder.

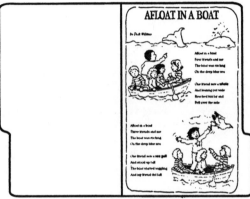 

One Page Story

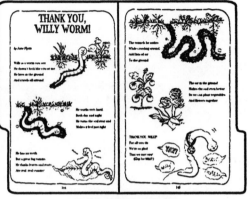

Two Page Story

For a 3-page story, use the 2 inside pages and the back page of the folder. For a 4-page story, use the front, inside, and back pages of the folder.

Felt Story Pieces

1. Duplicate the pattern pieces you need.

2. You could:

   - Color and cut out the paper patterns and back each one with a large piece of felt.

   - Get heavy-weight pellon at the fabric store, trace the patterns on the pellon, color them, and cut them out.

   - Create felt patterns, adding detail with colored markers or small pieces of felt glued to the main figure.

3. Put your FELT STORY PIECES in a recloseable plastic bag and attach it to your STORY FOLDER.

4. Store all the STORY FOLDERS in a large file box.

FALL

FLIP-FLOP SAVES THE CHILDREN

(Put Flip-Flop on right side of board.) Each day Flip-Flop Scarecrow stands straight and tall watching the fields. He is very proud of himself. He especially likes to be high in the air so he can see everything. He watches the corn growing in the fields, little animals running up and down the rows, and birds, geese, and airplanes flying overhead.

(Put farmhouse on left side of board.) One afternoon Flip-Flop was looking at the farmhouse. (Put 3 children near farmhouse.) He saw the farm children, Andrea, Kevin, and one of their friends playing tag in the yard. He watched them for awhile. (Put crow in sky.) Suddenly a big crow flew over the field. Flip-Flop looked away from the children and began waving his arms and legs and shouting at CROW to, *"Go away! Go away!"* Finally Flip-Flop frightened the bird out of the field.

He looked back at the farmyard. (Take children off board.) The children were not there. Flip-Flop wondered where they went. Maybe they went inside for a glass of water or a snack. He continued watching the cornfield and the farmyard. No more birds – no more children.

Flip-Flop began to worry about the children. They usually came back outside. Where were they? Suddenly he heard someone crying. (Put children next to Flip-Flop.) He looked into the field. He didn't see anyone, but someone must be there. He could still hear the crying.

He looked up and down the rows of corn, but no-one. This is strange. Then he heard a voice shouting at him, *"Flip-Flop, look straight down. We're at the bottom of your pole!"* Flip-Flop looked down. He saw the 3 children. They had wandered into the cornfield and had gotten lost. They were so scared. They could not see above the corn stalks to find their way home.

Flip-Flop said, *"Don't be scared, I'll help you. Start climbing up my pole. Hang onto my pants. When you get high enough, I'll grab you and put you on my shoulders."* One at a time the children climbed up Flip-Flop's legs. He grabbed Kevin and Andrea and put them on his shoulders. He said, *"Hang on tight, while I reach for your friend."* Flip-Flop grabbed the little boy and held him in his arms.

Now they were safe, but they had to get back home. Flip-Flop said, *"Let's all yell 'HELP US' as loud as we can. I'll count 1, 2, 3, then we'll yell."* Flip-Flop thought for a minute and said, *"I think we'll need more help to be sure your mom and dad hear us. Do you think the children listening to this story will help us?"* The three children shook their heads *"yes."*

"OK," said Flip-Flop. *"I'll count 1, 2, 3 everyone yell 'HELP US.'"* (Have your children yell out too.) The mom and dad ran out of the farmhouse as soon as they heard the children yelling for help. They saw the children sitting on top of Flip-Flop's shoulders. (Put tractor on board.) They hurried to the tractor and went out into the fields to get the children. After they were down safely, Mom and Dad looked up at Flip-Flop. *"What do you think they said to him?"* (Let children end the story.)

DIRECTIONS

Read the Safety Story. As you do put the felt pieces on the board.

TALK ABOUT THE STORY

"Have you ever been lost? How did you feel? Who found you?"

"If you get lost what should you do? Who could you ask for help?"

Practice dialing "911" with a friend.

STORY GAMES

Hide and Seek: Play this popular game on a warm, sunny day. When you find each person who is hiding, give him/her a big hug.

Visit the Police Station: Talk to the police officers about staying safe and what to do in case you get lost.

Make FELT PIECES

Flip-Flop on his pole
Farmhouse
Big crow
3 children (Kevin, Andrea, and their friend)
Tractor

FLIP-FLOP SAVES THE CHILDREN

FLIP-FLOP SAVES THE CHILDREN

FLIP-FLOP SAVES THE CHILDREN

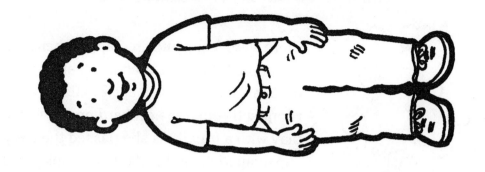

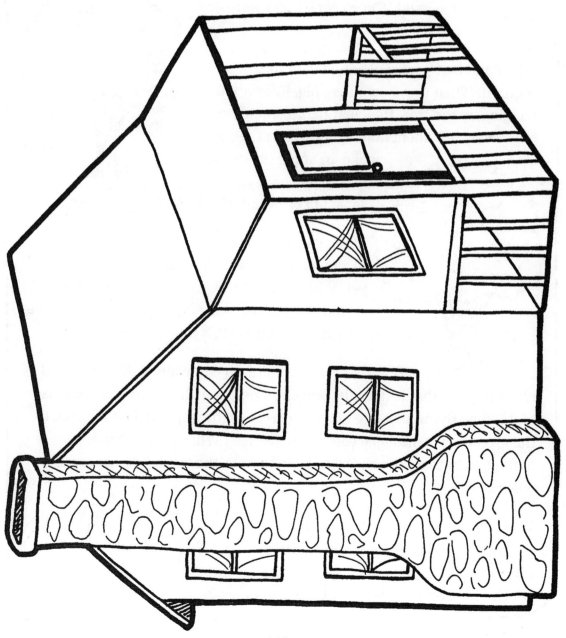

APPLE PICKING

There were 5 big, juicy red apples hanging on the apple tree in the orchard. (Put the tree on the board and then the 5 apples.) Carol was running through the orchard on her way to play with a friend. As she passed the tree, she jumped up and picked one apple for the two of them to share. (Have a child take one apple off the tree.) How many apples were left on the tree? Let's count. (Do it.) Now there were 4 apples on the tree.

Adam and Larry were playing tag in the orchard. When they saw those big, juicy apples hanging on the tree, they just had to each pick one. They took them home and helped their mom make an apple pie. (Have two children each pick an apple.) Let's count. (Do it.) Only 2 apples left.

Along came Tahasha who was walking her dog through the orchard. She had not had a snack yet. Who do you think was going to eat the next apple? (Let the children guess. Have a child pick one more apple.) Now there's only one apple.

Before any more children came along, Mrs. Squirrel ran out to get that last apple. She chomped and chomped and ate most of it. When the wind came along, the rest of the apple fell off the tree to the ground. (Put the apple core under the tree.) What do you think happened to that core as it was laying under the tree? (Talk about the possibilities.)

Well, during the night, a family of worms crawled right over and enjoyed every bit of it. In the morning, a bird came and got the stem and seeds in his beak and flew off.

DIRECTIONS

Enjoy this Number Story with the children. Have the children count the apples with you as the story progresses.

TALK ABOUT THE STORY

"Have you ever shared an apple with someone? Who?"

"Do you like to eat apple pie? Applesauce? Drink apple cider?"

STORY GAMES!

Apple Snack: Wash and cut several types of apples into narrow slices. As you eat your snack tell APPLE PICKING again.

Another Time: Drink apple cider while telling this story.

Apple Rhyme: Enjoy this rhyme.

WAY UP HIGH IN THE APPLE TREE

Way up high in the apple tree,
Two little apples smiled at me.
I shook that tree as hard as I could.
Down came the apples,
Um, um, good!

Make FELT PIECES

1 large apple tree
5 smiling apples
Family of worms
Apple core

APPLE PICKING

APPLE PICKING

DRIVE THE FIRE TRUCK

(tune: 1 Little, 2 Little, 3 Little Children)

Hurry, hurry, drive the fire truck.

Hurry, hurry, drive the fire truck.

Hurry, hurry, drive the fire truck.

On this sunny morning. (Change the weather to
your location.)

Hurry, hurry, turn the corner. (Tilt body.)

Hurry, hurry, turn the corner.

Hurry, hurry, turn the corner.

On this sunny morning.

Hurry, hurry, find the fire. (Put hand above eyes.)

Hurry, hurry, find the fire.

Hurry, hurry, find the fire.

On this sunny morning.

Hurry, hurry, spray the water. (Pretend to spray water.)

Hurry, hurry, spray the water.

Hurry, hurry, spray the water.

On this sunny morning.

Hurry, hurry, climb the ladder. (Hand over hand.)

Hurry, hurry, climb the ladder.

Hurry, hurry, climb the ladder.

On this sunny morning.

Slowly, slowly, back to the station. (Sing and drive very slowly.)

Slowly, slowly, back to the station.

Slowly, slowly, back to the station.

On this sunny morning.

DIRECTIONS

Put the 6 pictures, in the order they come in the story, face down on the floor in front of you. Just before you begin each verse of DRIVE THE FIRE TRUCK, put the appropriate picture on the felt board. Do the actions as you sing the story. When you are finished singing this Rhyme Story, you'll have the entire sequence on the felt board.

Talk About the Story

"How do firefighters help you when there is a fire?"

"If you hear the fire alarm what should you do?"

Talk about how fires start – matches, lighters, cigarettes, space heaters, etc.

STORY GAMES

Visit the Fire Station: Walk to a nearby fire station and have one of the firefighters show you the fire trucks, equipment, and special fire fighting gear.

Fire Drill: Pretend there is a fire. Practice exactly what you would do.

October is FIRE SAFETY MONTH: Sing DRIVE THE FIRE TRUCK several times each week.

Make FELT PIECES

1 copy of each of the 6 sequence cards. Back each with a large piece of felt.

DRIVE THE FIRE TRUCK

DRIVE THE FIRE TRUCK

DRIVE THE FIRE TRUCK

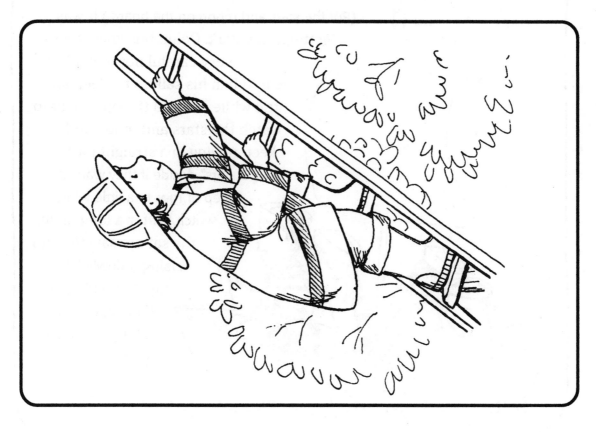

HAPPY COLUMBUS DAY

(Put the flag on the board.) The King and Queen of Spain gave Christopher Columbus the flag of Spain and enough money to sail to a new land that he had never seen before. He was so excited that he bought three ships, the Nina, the Pinta, and the Santa Maria. (Put 3 ships on the board.) Next he hired lots of sailors and bought food and supplies for a long voyage across the ocean. He would like you to be one of his sailors. Put on your sailor cap and climb aboard. (Put on caps.) Are you ready? (Answer.) Good!

The sailors were all very strong. They rowed and rowed until they got away from the city and out into the ocean. (Row. Keep rowing.) Christopher Columbus could feel the strong winds blowing his ships, so he called out to his sailors, *"Hoist all the sails! Pull the sails tight."* (Have the "sailors" put up the sails. Put a felt sail on each ship.)

(Put the stars and moon on the board.) It was getting very dark. Columbus knew they had to be very careful not to get lost. He told half his sailors to sleep for a little while. He told the other half to watch the stars and moon and keep rowing in a straight path. ("Sailors" decide if they want to sleep or row. In a little while switch.) After a long night, the sailors saw the sun rising. (Slowly take the stars and moon off the board and put the sun in the sky.)

After breakfast most of the sailors kept rowing, while others fished, cleaned the deck or straightened the sails. (Put dark clouds over ships.) All

of a sudden the sailors saw dark clouds in the sky and big waves coming towards the ships. The ocean was getting rough. Columbus yelled out, *"All sailors start rowing! There is a storm coming."* ("Sailors" jostle around as they row.) The ships went up and down in the waves. The sailors rowed hard while being tossed around by huge waves. Columbus yelled, *"Hang on until the storm goes away!"* Finally it did. (Put white clouds over the dark ones.) The dark clouds turned into white puffy ones, the huge waves became ripples, and the sailors rested on the deck. They were exhausted after rowing so hard. (Are the "sailors" tired?)

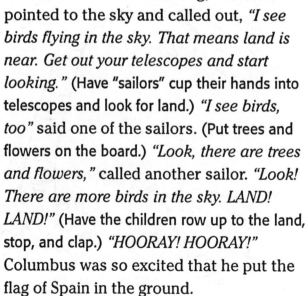

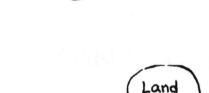

Columbus and his sailors kept sailing and sailing. (Put birds on the board.) One morning, Columbus pointed to the sky and called out, *"I see birds flying in the sky. That means land is near. Get out your telescopes and start looking."* (Have "sailors" cup their hands into telescopes and look for land.) *"I see birds, too"* said one of the sailors. (Put trees and flowers on the board.) *"Look, there are trees and flowers,"* called another sailor. *"Look! There are more birds in the sky. LAND! LAND!"* (Have the children row up to the land, stop, and clap.) *"HOORAY! HOORAY!"* Columbus was so excited that he put the flag of Spain in the ground.

DIRECTIONS

Put the felt pieces on the board as you tell the story. Let the children pretend they are sailors on one of Christopher Columbus' ships.

TALK ABOUT THE STORY

"Have you ever been on a boat? What kind of boat was it? Did you row the boat like the sailors with Christopher Columbus?"

STORY GAMES!

Row the Boat: Convert an appliance box into a boat. Let the children row, fish, and look for land.

Sail Your Ships: Put boats in a big sink or tub. Let the children pretend they are sailors as they sail their ships across the ocean.

Make FELT PIECES

3 ships
3 sails (Use the same
   sail pattern 3 times.)
Several stars
Moon
Sun
3-4 dark clouds
3-4 white clouds
Several birds
Several flowers
Tree
Spanish flag

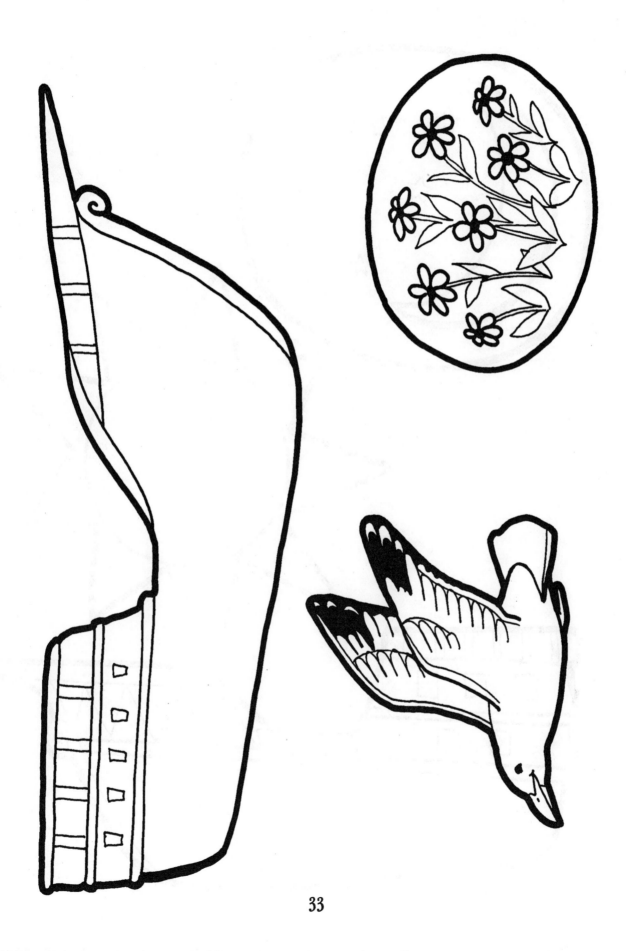

HAPPY COLUMBUS DAY

HAPPY COLUMBUS DAY

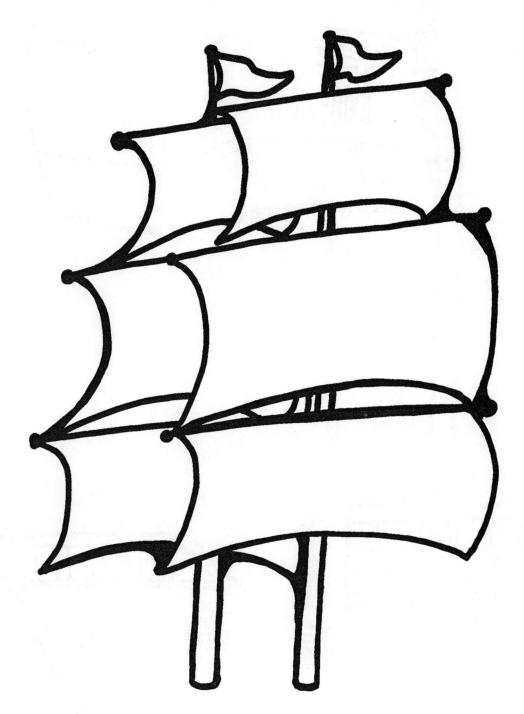

Make 3 sails.

HAPPY COLUMBUS DAY

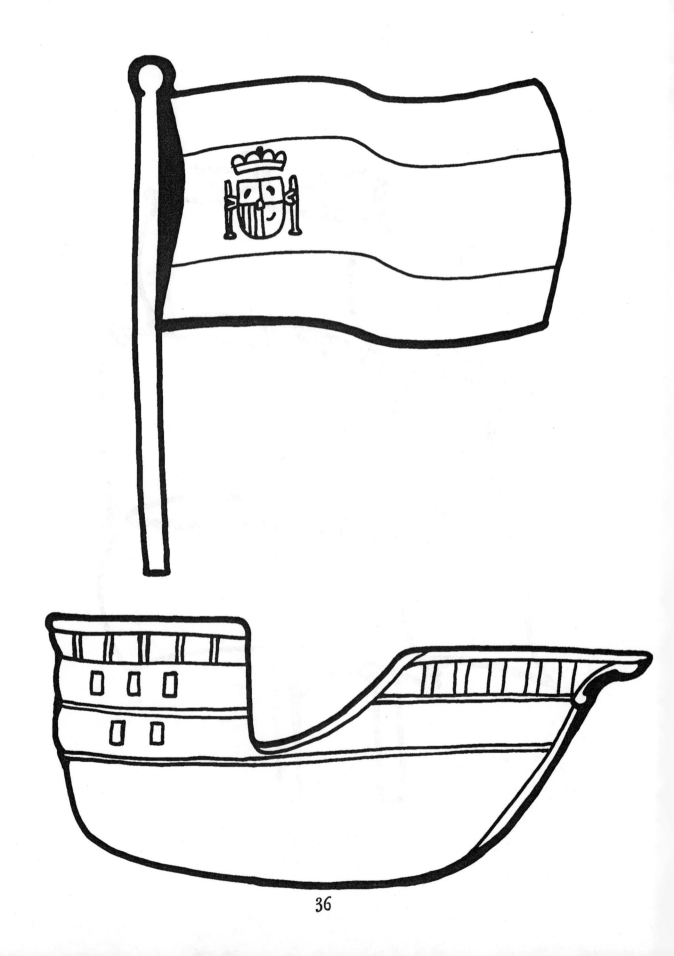

HAPPY COLUMBUS DAY

Make 3-4 white clouds.

Make several rain clouds.

BIRTHDAY DINNER
on the Parson Farm

(Put the barn and Farmer Parson on the board.) Farmer Parson had been working on the farm all day. Now he had one last chore, to feed the animals. He asked his daughter Samantha to help. (Put Samantha on board.) She loves feeding the animals, so she came running as soon as she heard her dad calling.

Samantha said, *"First, let's feed the animals who eat corn."* Samantha and her dad walked over to the chickens, pigs, and sheep. (Have children holding a chicken, pig, or sheep put it near the barn.) They tossed the animals lots of corn. In fact they had to go back for more.

The horses had been romping in the fields, chasing each other while waiting for their hay. The horses were really hungry. When they saw Samantha and her dad toss hay in the barn they ran in from the fields and waited for Farmer Parson to open the barn door. (Have children holding horses "run" them up to the barn.) Samantha and Farmer Parson led each horse into his stall. They were so hungry, they started eating their hay right away.

The geese and the ducks were not very patient. (Have children holding a goose or duck "waddle" him up to the barn for dinner.) They were crowing and quacking so loudly, telling Farmer Parson that they needed their seeds right now! Samantha ran over to them and said, *"My dad will be right here. Now quiet down and get ready to eat."* Farmer Parson came over to the barn door and threw their special seeds into the yard.

The cows and goats stayed in the fields. They had been eating grass all day and were so full! No dinner for them. (Have children holding cows and goats put them in the field away from the barn.)

The house pets were last. They ate in the farmhouse. (Take the barn and animals off the board. Put the farmhouse, Farmer Parson, Samantha, and the dog and cat on the felt board.) The dog ate her dog food and the cat had milk and cat food. After dinner they ran back outside for more running and chasing.

"All done. That was a BIG JOB! Thank you Samantha for helping me feed all our animals. Now it's our turn to have dinner," Farmer Parson said as he and Samantha walked into the farmhouse. They were very excited, for tonight was a special dinner for the Parson family. It was Samantha's birthday. She was 5 years old today.

Samantha had planned the dinner. She picked CORN for her favorite vegetable. When she saw it on the table, she laughed at her dad and said, *"I like the same food as the chicken, pigs, and sheep."* (Ask the children, "What other foods do you think Samantha picked for her birthday dinner? Were any others the same as the animals? What about the cat's milk?")

After dinner they had Samantha's favorite birthday dessert. Do you know what it was? (Children call out. Put the birthday cake on the felt board.) How many candles do you think went on her cake? (Call out.) You guessed it – 5. (Count as you put the candles on the cake.) Let's all sing HAPPY BIRTHDAY to Samantha and then help her blow out her candles. (Do it.)

DIRECTIONS

Put the barn in the middle of the felt board and Farmer Parson and Samantha off to the side. Pass out the felt animal pieces to the children.

When it's time for Samantha's birthday party, take the barn and animals off the felt board and put the farmhouse, Farmer Parson, Samantha, and "birthday" pieces on the board.

TALK ABOUT THE STORY

"Who comes to your birthday party?"

"Do you plan your birthday dinner? Who helps you? What do you like? Do you have birthday cake or something else for dessert?"

STORY GAMES

Pretend Party: Put on birthday hats, sing Happy Birthday to everyone, and have a special snack.

Make FELT PIECES

Farmer Parson
Samantha
5 birthday candles
Birthday cake
Barn
Farmhouse
Dog
Chicken/s
Pig/s
Horse/s
Goose/geese
Duck/s
Cow/s
Goat/s
Cat
Sheep

BIRTHDAY DINNER on the Parson Farm

BIRTHDAY DINNER on the Parson Farm

BIRTHDAY DINNER on the Parson Farm

BIRTHDAY DINNER on the Parson Farm

Make 5 candles.

BIRTHDAY DINNER on the Parson Farm

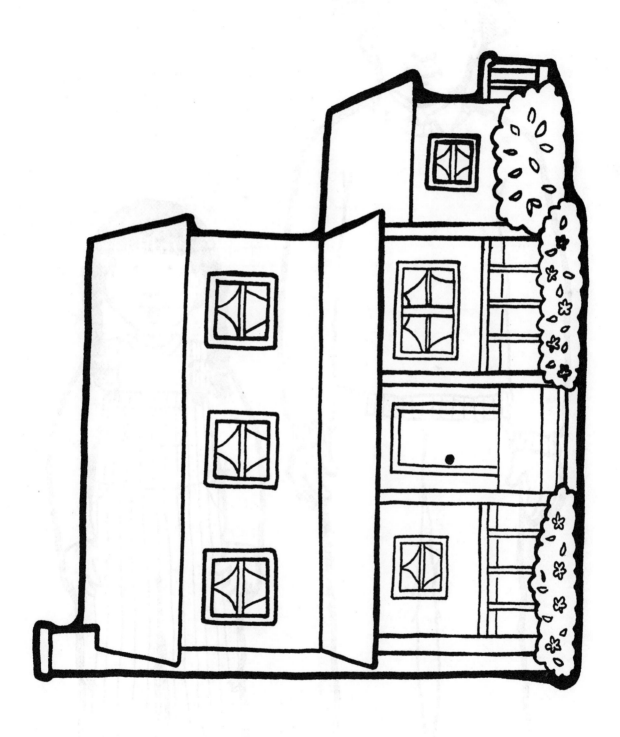

BIRTHDAY DINNER on the Parson Farm

BIRTHDAY DINNER on the Parson Farm

IF I KNEW YOU WERE COMING!

(Tune: If I Knew You Were Coming)

If I knew you were coming, I'd have set the table,

Set the table, set the table.

If I knew you were coming, I'd have set the table,

Howdy do, Howdy do, Howdy do!

If I knew you were coming, I'd have stuffed the turkey,

Stuffed the turkey, stuffed the turkey.

If I knew you were coming, I'd have stuffed the turkey,

Howdy do, Howdy do, Howdy do!

Continue Singing:

Mashed the potatoes…

Baked a pie…

Squished the squash…

Chopped the slaw…

Kneaded some bread…

Poured the milk… (Add the children's ideas!)

Last Verse   (Sing slowly.)

We're all so tired that we'll say *"Good-bye,"*

Say *"Good-bye,"* say *"Good-bye."*

We're all so tired that we'll say *"Good-bye,"*

Howdy do, Howdy do, Howdy do! (Slowly wave as you sing last line.)

DIRECTIONS

With all the fall and winter holidays, the children and their families will have lots of people visiting. Talk about different things they do to get ready for company.

Sing this Song Story about how they get ready for visitors. Start with some common activities, continue with things particular to Thanksgiving or any holiday your children celebrate, and conclude with your children's ideas.

Put the felt pieces on the "holiday table" (felt board) as you sing each stanza. When children say their ideas, write each one on an index card and put on the felt board.

TALK ABOUT THE STORY

"How is your family going to celebrate Thanksgiving?" (Other holiday)

"Are you going to eat at someone else's house? Who's? Who will be there?"

"What do you think you'll have to eat?"

STORY GAMES!

Turkey, Turkey, Where Are Your Feathers: Stand in a circle. One child struts around the circle, stopping at a friend to ask, *"Turkey, turkey, where are your feathers?"* The child responds, *"I don't know but I'll go see."* That child fans out his hands behind him and struts to another child, asking the same question. Continue in this manner. The last child struts to the adult who answers, *"Here they are"* as she pulls out craft feathers and gives one to each player.

Set the Table: Have all the things you need to set one place at a table. Name each item and talk about it. Have the children pretend they are setting the table. What do you start with? Continue until the table is all set. (Talk about setting the table next time you have a meal together.)

Make FELT PIECES

Pretend your felt board is the holiday table

Turkey on a platter	Head of cabbage
Mashed potatoes	Loaf of bread
Pie	Glass of milk
Squash	Index cards with felt on the back

Make place cards.

Grandma

49

IF I KNEW YOU WERE COMING!

TOM TURKEY

TOM TURKEY was moping around the barnyard. All his farm friends had bright, beautiful colors. He only had plain brown feathers.

As he walked past the hen house, he could hear the hens squawking, *"Oh, there goes TOM TURKEY. Too bad he has all brown feathers. He needs some white feathers like ours."* Like magic, one of TOM'S feathers turned white. He turned his head and looked. He smiled as he saw his new feather. He started walking a little taller and prouder.

Then he began thinking, I bet I look silly with all brown feathers and a white one. I'll go find GREEN TURTLE and ask her opinion. TOM walked down to the pond. There was GREEN TURTLE lying on a log in the sun. TOM called, *"GREEN TURTLE, do I look silly with one white feather and lots of brown ones?"* GREEN TURTLE took one look at TOM and almost started to laugh, but didn't. *"Yes you do TOM. Let me help."* As soon as she spoke, one of TOM'S brown feathers turned green. *"Now you look much better, TOM. I gave you a green feather to go with your white one."* He looked at his reflection in the pond. Yes, he was much more handsome.

As he proudly walked away from the pond, he began thinking again. One white feather and one green feather, but still, lots of brown feathers. I know, I'll go ask YELLOW CHICK and ORANGE DUCK what they think. TOM found his friends walking past the barn door. As soon as they saw him, YELLOW CHICK called out, *"TOM, where did you get your white and green feathers?"* Before TOM could answer, CHICK said, *"You need a yellow feather!"* ORANGE DUCK called out, *"and an orange one."* In a flash TOM had a yellow and orange feather. *"Oh TOM, now you look much better!"*

TOM was beginning to like his new look. As he walked, all the animals looked at him. They said, *"Oh TOM, you are very handsome."* Just then BLUE BIRD flew over the barnyard. *"Heh, TOM, what are you doing to your feathers?"* TOM called out, *"All my barnyard friends are sharing their colors with me. How do you like them?"* *"I think they look great, but you need a blue one."* Before BLUE BIRD had flown away, TOM had a blue feather to add to his other colors.

FARMER DUGAN walked out of the barn door as TOM was walking by. He said, *"Well TOM TURKEY, it looks like you have had a busy day. I saw you this morning. You had plain brown feathers. Now you are strutting around with brown, yellow, green, orange, white, and blue ones. What happened?"* He told FARMER DUGAN about his day.

FARMER DUGAN asked TOM if he'd like some more colors. *"I think that would be fine. I'll look even better."* FARMER DUGAN asked TOM what colors he would like. *"Well, I think I'd like red and black."* FARMER DUGAN said, *"Wait right here. Let me see if two of my farm friends can help you."* FARMER DUGAN called FRECKLES the farm cat and BLAZE the dog. FARMER DUGAN asked the two animals if they could share some of their color with TOM. *"Of course we can,"* they said together. And just like before, TOM had two more colors. FRECKLES gave him a black feather and BLAZE gave him a red one.

TOM looked over his shoulder to see all his new colors. He said to himself. *"I really like my new colors, but I don't look too much like a turkey any more. What should I do?"* At that moment WISE OWL landed on the fence. She said, *"TOM, what happened to you? I hardly knew you with all those colors."* TOM told WISE OWL that he was getting very tired of his plain brown feathers. His friends had been so nice to share their bright colors with him. WISE OWL said, *"Try this TOM."* As she spoke, all TOM's feathers changed back to brown, but with splotches of color on the tips of each one.

TOM smiled a thank you at WISE OWL and proudly strutted from one end of the barnyard to the other.

DIRECTIONS

Put TOM TURKEY on the felt board. Read the story, adding the felt animal pieces, as you go.

TALK ABOUT THE STORY

"If you were TOM TURKEY, would you want all your feathers full of color or just the tips of each one? Why?"

"If you were one of the farm animals would you have shared your color with TOM? What color would you have given him?"

STORY GAMES!

Feathers for TOM TURKEY: Cut a large turkey body and lots of feathers to match the colors in the story. Put the turkey on the table/floor. Hand all the feathers to the players. Say *"If you have a blue feather, give it to TOM."* Continue until TOM has all his feathers.

Make FELT PIECES

Moping TOM TURKEY
Happy TOM TURKEY
Farmer Dugan
White hen
Green turtle
Yellow chick
Blue bird
Red Irish setter
Black cat
Wise owl on a fence

TOM TURKEY

TOM TURKEY

TOM TURKEY

WINTER

FLIP-FLOP LOVES HIS FRIENDS

Flip-Flop loves the **stars and moon** who keep him company at night.

Flip-Flop loves **farm rooster** who wakes him up every morning.

Flip-Flop loves the **bull frogs** who sing him to sleep every night.

Flip-Flop loves the **ladybugs** who use their spots to teach him to count.

Flip-Flop loves the **rain** for keeping him cool and clean.

Flip-Flop loves the **fireflies** who light the path to his friend's fields at night.

Flip-Flop loves the **butterflies** who teach him his colors.

Flip-Flop loves the **dirt** for helping him stand up straight all day.

Flip-Flop loves the **clouds** for blocking the hot sun.

Flip-Flop loves the **caterpillars** who make him laugh as they tickle his arms and legs.

Flip-Flop loves the **farm dog**, Blaze, who protects the farm and animals.

HAPPY VALENTINE'S DAY, EVERYONE!!
Love, Flip-Flop

P.S. Write FLIP-FLOP a letter and tell him who you love and why. Send your letter/drawing to:

FLIP-FLOP SCARECROW • 38W567 Brindlewood • Elgin, Illinois 60123

DIRECTIONS

Duplicate the hearts. Color if you want. Glue a large piece of felt on the back of each one. Put each heart on the felt board as you read this Valentine Story.

TALK ABOUT THE STORY

"Who you love? Do you love the same people and things as Flip-Flop?"

STORY GAMES

Valentine Cards: Fold a piece of paper in half. Make a Valentine Card for someone you love.

Letter to FLIP-FLOP: Encourage children to "write" a letter or draw pictures of people they love. Send the letters/drawings to Flip-Flop. His address is:

> FLIP-FLOP SCARECROW
> 38W567 Brindlewood
> Elgin IL 60123

Make FELT PIECES

11 message hearts

FLIP-FLOP LOVES HIS FRIENDS

Flip-Flop loves the **stars and moon** who keep him company at night.

Flip-Flop loves **farm rooster** who wakes him up every morning.

Flip-Flop loves the **bull frogs** who sing him to sleep every night.

Flip-Flop loves the **ladybugs** who use their spots to teach him to count.

FLIP-FLOP LOVES HIS FRIENDS

Flip-Flop loves the **rain** for keeping him cool and clean.

Flip-Flop loves the **fireflies** who light the path to his friend's fields at night.

FLIP-FLOP LOVES HIS FRIENDS

Flip-Flop loves the **butterflies** who teach him his colors.

Flip-Flop loves the **clouds** for blocking the hot sun.

Flip-Flop loves the **caterpillars** who make him laugh as they tickle his arms and legs.

Flip-Flop loves the **farm dog**, Blaze, who protects the farm and animals.

Flip-Flop loves
the **dirt** for helping
him stand up
straight all day.

OLD ST. NICHOLAS

(tune: Old McDonald Had a Farm)

Old St. Nicholas had a tree (Form tree with arms.)
Ho, ho, ho, ho, ho.
And on his tree he had some HORNS, (Blow horns.)
Ho, ho, ho, ho, ho.
With a toot-toot here, (Blow horns to one side.)
And a toot-toot there, (Blow horns to other side.)
Here a toot, there a toot (Blow horns to both sides.)
Everywhere a toot-toot. (Blow horns every direction.)

Old St. Nicholas had a tree (Form tree with arms.)
Ho, ho, ho, ho, ho.

And on his tree he had some LIGHTS,
   (Open/close hands quickly.)
Ho, ho, ho, ho, ho.
With a flash-flash here, (Flash hands to one side.)
And a flash-flash there, (Flash hands to other side.)
Here a flash, there a flash (Flash hands to both sides.)
Everywhere a flash-flash. (Flash hands everywhere.)

Old St. Nicholas had a tree (Form tree with arms.)
Ho, ho, ho, ho, ho.
And on his tree he had some CANDY CANES, (Pat tummy.)
Ho, ho, ho, ho, ho.
With a yum-yum here, (Pat tummy on one side then other.)
Etc.

Old St. Nicholas had a tree (Form tree with arms.)
Ho, ho, ho, ho, ho.
And on his tree he had some DRUMS, (Slap thighs.)
Ho, ho, ho, ho, ho.
With a boom-boom here, (Slap thighs on one side
   and then other.)
Etc.

Old St. Nicholas had a tree (Form tree with arms.)
Ho, ho, ho, ho, ho.
And on his tree he had some BELLS, (Ring a bell.)
Ho, ho, ho, ho, ho.
With a ring-ring here, (Ring a bell on one side and
    then other.)
Etc.

Old St. Nicholas had a tree, (Form tree with arms.)
  Ho, ho, ho, ho, ho.
  And on his tree he had some SNOWFLAKES,
    (Wiggle fingers.)
  Ho, ho, ho, ho, ho.
  With a flutter-flutter here, (Wiggle fingers on one
    side then other.)
      Etc.

Old St. Nicholas had a tree, (Form tree
    with arms.)
Ho, ho, ho, ho, ho.
And on his tree he had some BIRDS,
    ("Flap" arms.)
Ho, ho, ho, ho, ho.
With a peep-peep here, (Open and close
    hands on one side then the other.)
Etc.

Old St. Nicholas had a tree, (Form tree with arms.)
  Ho, ho, ho, ho, ho.
 And on his tree he had a STAR, (Blink eyes.)
  Ho, ho, ho, ho, ho.
    With a twinkle-twinkle here, (Turn head as you
        blink eyes to one side and then other.)
      Etc.

DIRECTIONS

Put the evergreen tree on the felt board. Hang the ornaments as you sing OLD ST. NICHOLAS.

Let the children use their hands and pretend they are the ornaments. When the Song Story is over, your tree will be all trimmed!!

TALK ABOUT THE STORY

"Tell me about the Christmas tree in your house."

"Have you seen the Christmas tree in the shopping mall?"

STORY GAMES!

Sing Holiday Songs: Sing the children's favorite songs.

Ornaments for the Birds: Cut out posterboard evergreen shapes. Punch a hole in the top of each one and string a piece of yarn through it. Have the children "paint" the shapes with peanut butter and then sprinkle bird seed on them.
Hang in the trees for the birds to peck at and enjoy.

Make FELT PIECES

Large evergreen tree
Horn
Lights
Candy cane
Drum
Bell
Snowflakes
Bird
Star

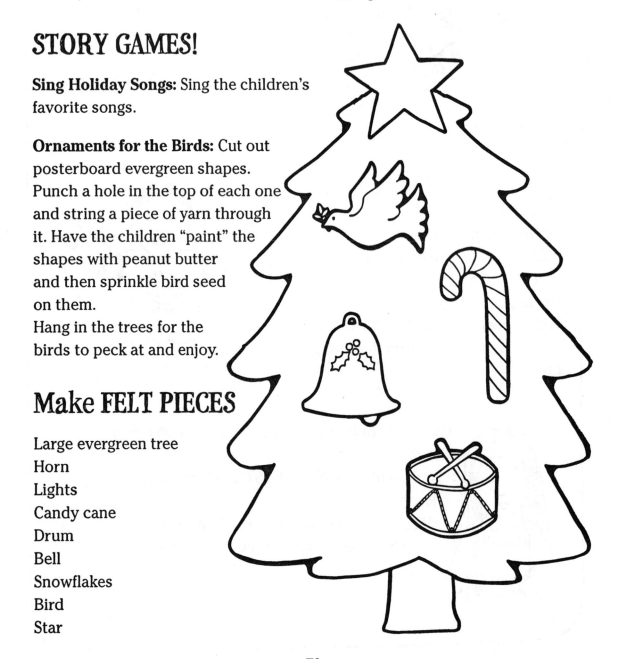

OLD ST. NICHOLAS

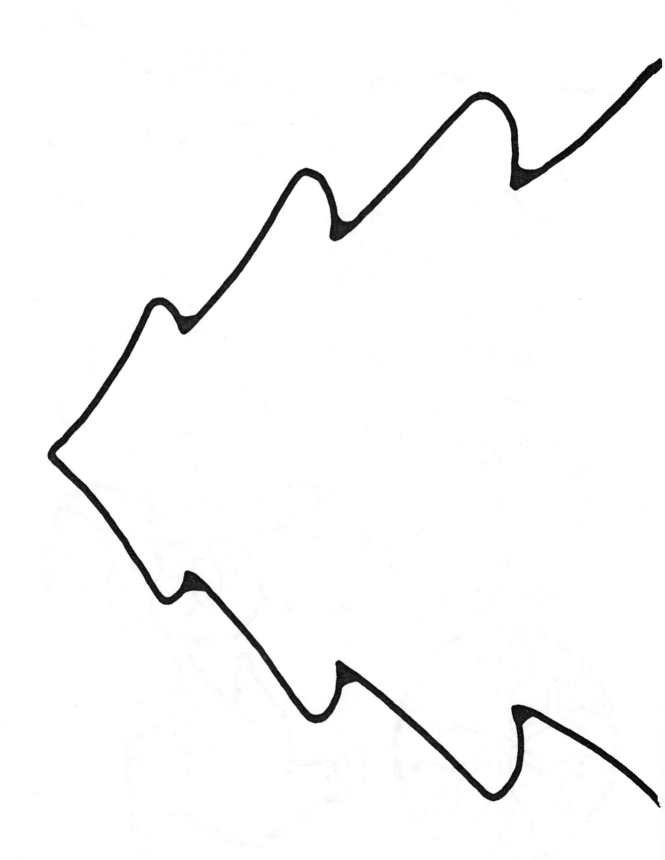

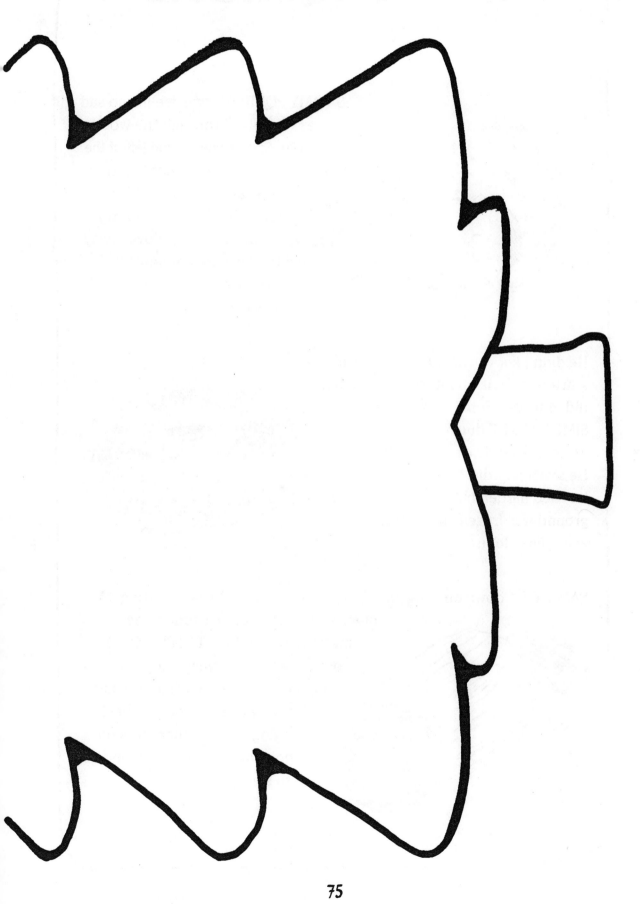

SAMMY SQUIRREL

by Jane Flynn

SAMMY SQUIRREL was feeling so sad as he walked through the woods. (Put Sad Sammy on the left of the felt board.) It was winter. (Put snowflakes on the board.) The weather was cold and snowy. The fall winds had blown away all the leaves from SAMMY'S favorite trees. Now he needed a new place to live.

He didn't know where to find a home. He started to think about what his friends did in winter. Some of them, like SIMON SNAKE dug holes in the ground. SAMMY decided to try that. He started to dig. It was difficult, so he tried harder, but still no luck. The ground was frozen and he couldn't even dig a door.

SAMMY sat down on a log and thought some more. He was getting colder and colder. All of a sudden he remembered that SYLVESTER SKUNK found a winter home in a log with a big hole. He jumped right up and looked at the log he had been sitting on. But, there was no hole for him to curl up and go to sleep.

SAMMY thought about BETSY BEAR who slept in a cave. But there were no caves in SAMMY'S forest. Then he remembered that FERNANDO FROG lived under the mud near the pond. SAMMY didn't think that would be such a good idea. He started to shiver when he thought of living near icy cold water.

What he really wanted was a tree to keep him warm and protect him from the wind. Suddenly, as he was walking, he noticed something green in the distance. (Slowly start to pull the tree out of the folder.) As he got closer, he realized that the green was a big soft evergreen tree! (Pull the tree out of the folder and put it on the felt board.) SAMMY was so happy! (Take sad Sammy away. Put happy Sammy next to the tree.) He quickly scampered up the trunk of the evergreen tree and found the biggest branch in the tree. YES! A perfect spot to live all winter! (Tuck Sammy in the tree.)

SAMMY was so tired that he fell asleep. As he slept, the wind blew even harder and the temperature got even colder, but SAMMY SQUIRREL was safe and warm tucked inside the nice soft pine needles of his favorite evergreen branch. (Clap quietly for Sammy. Remember, he's sleeping.)

DIRECTIONS

Put the large evergreen tree inside a folder with the top of the tree barely showing. Have the other felt pieces nearby. Put them on the board as you read/tell the story.

TALK ABOUT THE STORY

"How do you stay warm in winter?"

"If SAMMY hadn't found a warm tree, where else do you think he could have lived and kept warm?"

STORY GAMES!

Time To Hibernate: Get several boxes large enough for a child to comfortably sit in. Add a pillow, stuffed animal, blanket, etc. Let children pretend they are animals hibernating in the winter.

Make FELT PIECES

Sad SAMMY
Happy SAMMY
Skunk
Snake
Bear
Frog
Large evergreen tree
6-8 snowflakes

SAMMY SQUIRREL

SAMMY SQUIRREL

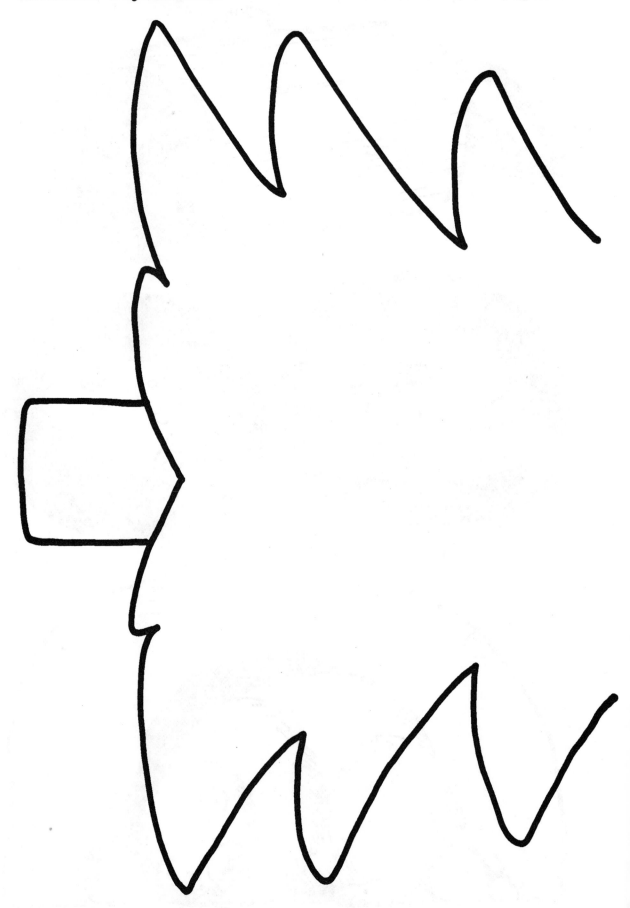

SAMMY SQUIRREL

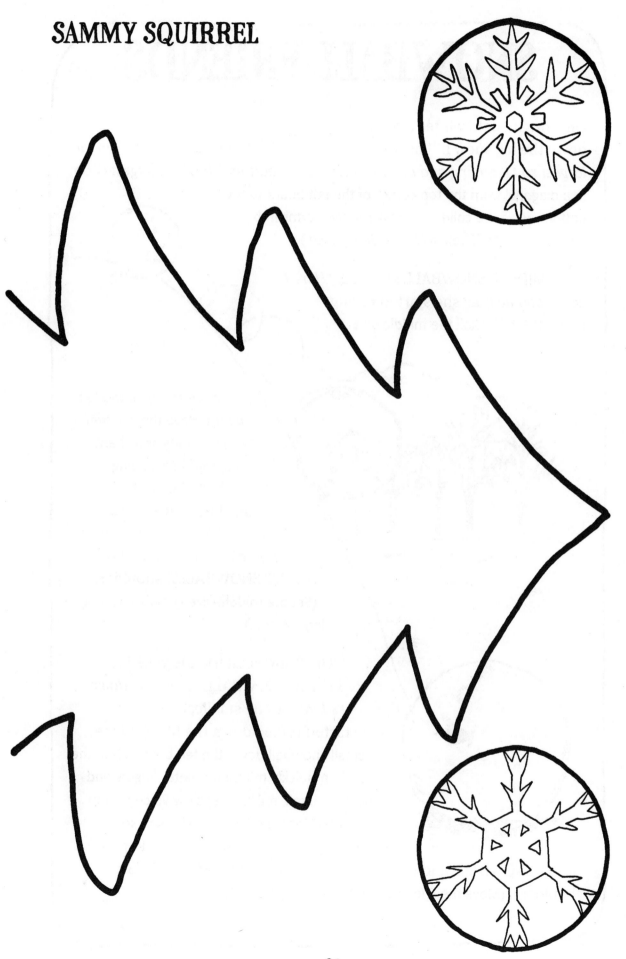

SNOWBALL FRIENDS

On a bright, cold winter morning, 3 snowball friends decided to roll down the big snow hill near their home. GIANT SNOWBALL said, *"I'm the largest so I'll go first and meet you two at the bottom."* (Roll the largest circle in a diagonal from the top corner of the felt board to the bottom. Have the children slowly roll their arms in big circles. Chant "roll, roll, roll" in a deep voice.)

Then MIDDLE SNOWBALL shouted, *"Here I cooooooome!!"* as she started rolling down the hill. (Roll the middle-size snowball down the felt board. Have the children roll their hands and chant "roll, roll, roll" in a singing voice.) When she got to the bottom, she bumped into GIANT SNOWBALL and said, *"Hi friend"* as she climbed onto GIANT SNOWBALL'S shoulders. (Set the middle-size snowball on the largest one.)

The 2 snowball friends yelled to LITTLE SNOWBALL *"Come on down, it's fun!"* So the smallest snowball started rolling down the hill. (Roll the small snowball down the felt board. Have the children quickly roll their pointer fingers and chant "roll, roll, roll" in a speedy voice.) Soon he banged into his friends. He was so excited to see them that he jumped up onto GIANT SNOWBALL and then climbed onto MIDDLE SNOWBALL'S shoulders. (Move the snowball to the top as you talk.)

"It's really high up here" said LITTLE SNOWBALL. *"I can see inside this window."* (Put the 2 children on felt board.) *"Two children are getting ready to come outside and play in the snow. The girl has a silly hat in her hand. What do you think she is going to do with it?" "I don't know,"* said GIANT SNOWBALL. *"Let's watch her."*

The two children opened the door and ran as fast as they could to SNOWMAN. The little girl stood on her tiptoes and stretched so high, trying to put the hat on SNOWMAN'S head. Her brother shouted, *"Reach just a little more!"* She stretched even higher. (Put hat on snowman's head.) As she did, SNOWMAN gently bowed his head just enough so she could place the hat on his head. *"Yeah, you did it,"* shouted her brother! *"I'm so excited. We have a SNOWMAN right in our own yard. Let's keep dressing him."* (Talk with the children about what other clothes and features the children could use to finish their SNOWMAN.)

DIRECTIONS

Put the 3 snowballs in the upper-left hand corner of the felt board and the hat and 2 children tucked under your leg.

In the story, the 3 snowballs roll down a hill. As you are "rolling" the snowballs down the hill, have your children roll their arms, hands or fingers and chant, *"roll, roll, roll, roll…"* until each snowball has reached the bottom.

TALK ABOUT THE STORY

"Tell me about a snow pal that you have made. Did your pal have a hat?"

"What games did you play with your snow pal? Which one was your favorite?"

STORY GAMES!

Build Inside Snow Pals: Fill a large dish tub full of snow. Build snow figures inside. (Remember to wear mittens.)

Magic Hats: Put on your magic hats, start the music, and dance around the room. Change the music and dance again.

Make FELT PIECES

1, 8" circle
1, 6" circle
1, 4" circle
Hat
2 children

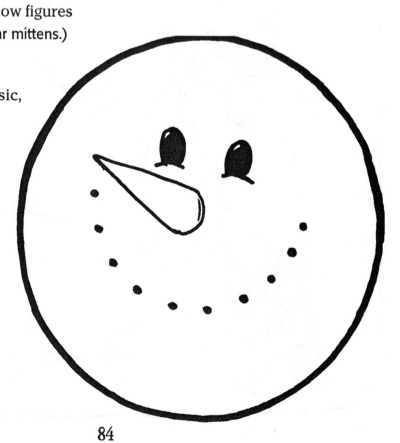

SNOWBALL FRIENDS

DRESS FROSTY

It was a cold winter day. The children had just finished building a giant FROSTY. Now they wanted to dress him. See if you can guess what clothes the children put on FROSTY.

● I sit on top of FROSTY'S head. I am black. What am I? (Hat.)

● I help keep FROSTY'S neck warm. I am red with yellow strips. What do you think I am? (Scarf.)

● Speaking of keeping FROSTY warm, I cover his chest and arms. I don't want him to catch cold. What am I? (Jacket.)

● When the wind blows, FROSTY'S jacket would blow off it weren't for us. We are very important to keeping him warm and cozy. Besides we are big and colorful so everyone sees us. What are we? (Buttons.)

● FROSTY loves to play catch with his snow pals in the neighborhood. We keep his hands warm so he can play for a long time. What do you think we are? (Mittens.)

● We are very important. We keep FROSTY'S feet dry. We are made of rubber. What are we? (Boots.)

● At the end of the day FROSTY does his chores. His first job is to clean all the snow off the sidewalks. He uses me to do this job. What do you think I am? (Snow shovel.)

FROSTY is all dressed. He's ready to play snow games with all the other snow pals and the children in the neighborhood. What do you think they'll play? Remember FROSTY'S favorite game is "Catch the Snow Balls." What else do you think they will play? (Let the children think about all of their favorite things to do in the snow. Talk about them and decide if they think FROSTY would like to play also.)

DIRECTIONS

Put FROSTY on the felt board. Pass out all the clothes and pieces to the children. Tell this Riddle Story. As you tell the story have the child with the appropriate piece DRESS FROSTY. (If you have a large group have 2 sets of Frosty and clothes.)

TALK ABOUT THE STORY

"Tell me about times that you've built a real snow pal outside. How tall was it? Was it a snow animal? Did you give your character a face? Clothes? Broom? What else?"

"Have you ever watched the story of Frosty the Snowman on television? Did you like it?"

STORY GAMES!

Indoor Snow Pals: Have white play dough along with a tray of Frosty items, such as coffee stir sticks, buttons, toothpicks, scraps of posterboard, etc. Encourage children to build lots of Frostys.

Sing: Teach the children the Frosty the Snowman song.

Make FELT PIECES

Large Frosty
Jacket
Buttons
Snow shovel
Black hat
Boots
Red and yellow scarf
Mittens
Stick arms

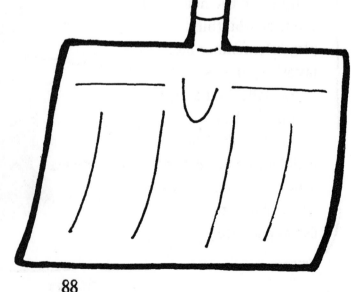

DRESS FROSTY

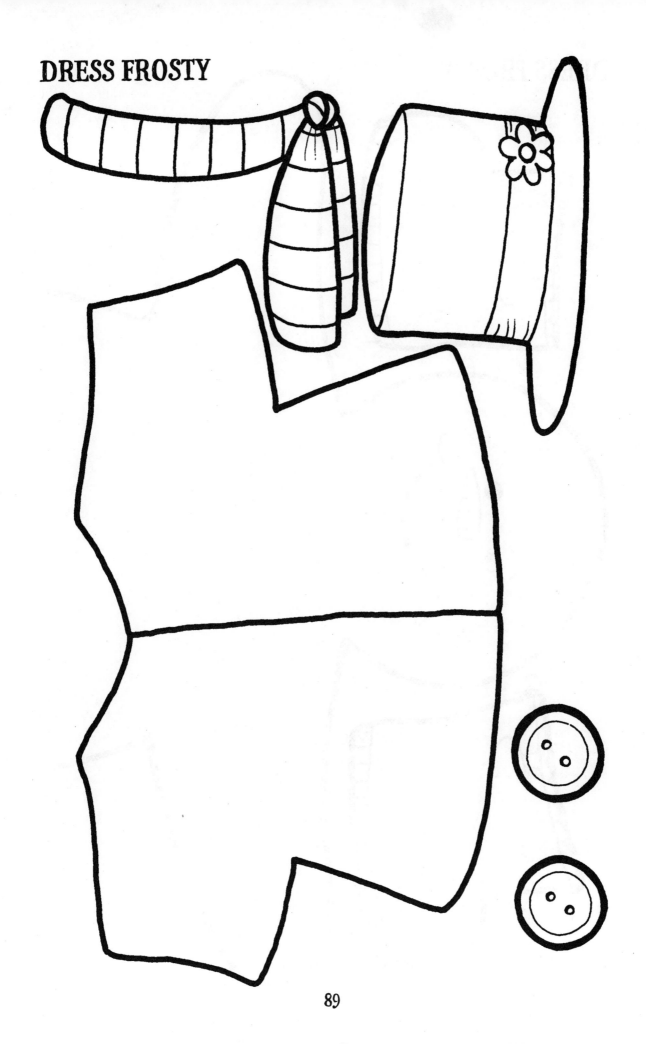

DRESS FROSTY

DRESS FROSTY

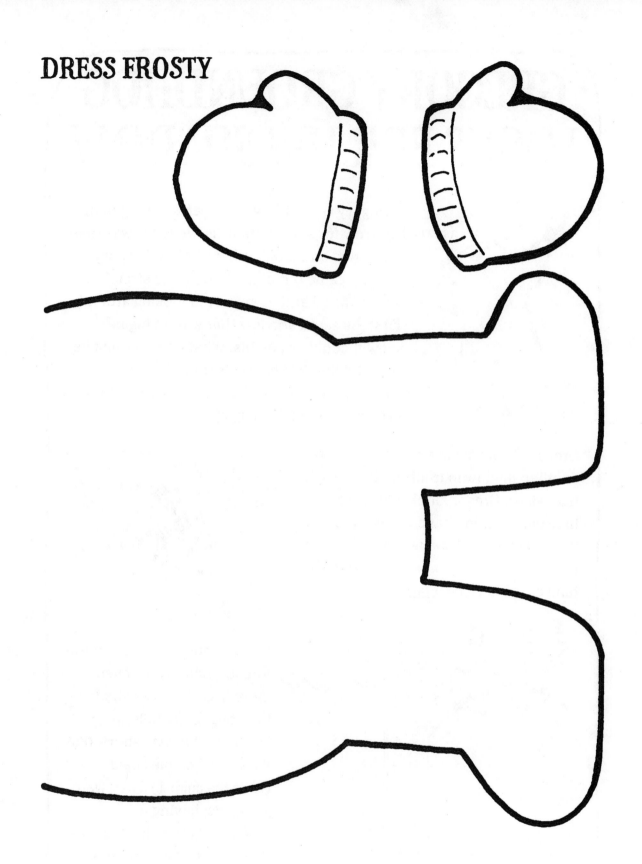

GREGORY GROUNDHOG LOOKS FOR HIS SHADOW

Yawn!

Gregory Groundhog had been sleeping in his burrow for several months. He felt it was time to get up and look for his shadow. Gregory slowly came out of his burrow. He stretched and yawned and then started looking around. First, he saw a shadow that was so big he knew it could not be his. What do you think he saw? (Let the children name some large animals then put the bear on the board and everyone call out what it is.) It was a huge <u>bear</u>.

Gregory kept walking until he noticed another shadow in front of him. This one had wings. Gregory looked down at himself. He didn't have wings. What could it be? (Put the bird on the board and let the children name it.) *"I know"* he said to himself, *"It must be a <u>bird</u>."*

He continued on through the forest. There were several more friends. Their shadows had long, fluffy tails. Gregory's tail was short. (Put the squirrel on the board. Name the animal.) They were <u>squirrels</u>, having a wonderful time chasing up, down, and all around the trees.

Gregory thought it was very strange that he was seeing everyone's shadow but his own. *"I'd better try a little harder,"* he said to himself. With a smile on his face, he started walking. Soon he came to a pond. He thought maybe he would see his shadow reflecting in the water. But no, it wasn't there. The first thing he saw was a moving shadow taking giant leaps from rock to rock. *"What could that be?"* Gregory wondered. It stopped moving and he instantly recognized it. (Talk about what the children think Gregory saw. Put the frog on the board.) *"It was a frog."* He laughed to himself as he moved on.

As Gregory was walking along the bank, he noticed another moving shadow. This one moved very slowly, not quickly like the frog. He thought for a minute. (Talk about which of Gregory's friends this was. Put the turtle on the board.) Then he remembered that this animal was called a <u>turtle</u>.

Speaking of pokey friends, there went a long skinny friend slipping through the grass. (What animal would slither through the grass? Put the snake on the board. Let the children call out who it was.) Yes, it was a <u>snake</u>.

Well, he was having no luck finding his shadow at the pond, so he walked back into the forest. There to greet him was his fast hopping friend with long ears. (Who do the children think it was? Put the rabbit on the board.) It was <u>Mrs. Rabbit</u>. Gregory asked Mrs. Rabbit where his shadow could be. She said, *"Follow me, Gregory."* Off they went.

"Wait," Gregory called, *"I see a huge shadow with long legs and antlers, maybe it's mine!"* They stopped. Gregory and Mrs. Rabbit started laughing. (Ask the children if they know who this forest friend could be. Put the deer on the board.) Gregory felt silly thinking that the big shadow of the <u>deer</u> was his.

Gregory took another step. In front of him was a smaller shadow. Yes, this could be his. He looked closely. Oops, the shadow had six legs and was really small. (What animal do the children think Gregory saw now. Put the ant on the board.) Once again Gregory felt very silly. This was a shadow of an <u>ant</u>. Gregory kept looking. All of a sudden the sun shone brightly. Gregory looked off to his left side. What he saw was a <u>black shadow</u>. It scared him so much that he didn't have much time to think or even to say "thank you" to Mrs. Rabbit.

He quickly <u>ran past</u> Mrs. Rabbit, <u>jumped over</u> the ant, <u>squeezed under</u> the deer, <u>scurried around</u> the snake, <u>tiptoed over</u> the turtle, <u>splashed through</u> the pond and scared that leaping frog. He <u>scampered past</u> the squirrels, <u>frightened</u> the bird, and <u>dodged</u> the bear. He ran directly toward his burrow and <u>scooted down</u> his hole as quickly as he could. There he felt very secure and warm. After he had caught his breath, he realized that he had been tricked once again. This time by his very own shadow!! (Put Gregory Groundhog's shadow on the board.)

94

DIRECTIONS

Put all the animal pieces in the order they come in the story.

Talk with the children about hibernation. Then, tell them this Fill-in-the-Blank Story. As you do, put each animal on the board as you name it.

Read the last paragraph quickly so the children get the feeling of GREGORY hurrying back to his burrow. Have the children help GREGORY run faster by slapping their thighs as you read!

TALK ABOUT THE STORY

"GREGORY GROUNDHOG had lots of friends in the story. Let's try to name all of them."

"Who was his largest friend? Smallest friend?"

"If you were GREGORY, do you think you would have been scared by your own shadow?"

STORY GAMES!

Shadow Walk: On a sunny day take a neighborhood walk. Look for your own shadows.

Indoor Shadows: Have one person shine a flashlight on a wall. Have several others make silly shadows in the light.

Make FELT PIECES

Shadow of Gregory Groundhog
Gregory Groundhog
Bear
Bird
Squirrel
Frog
Turtle
Snake
Rabbit
Deer
Ant

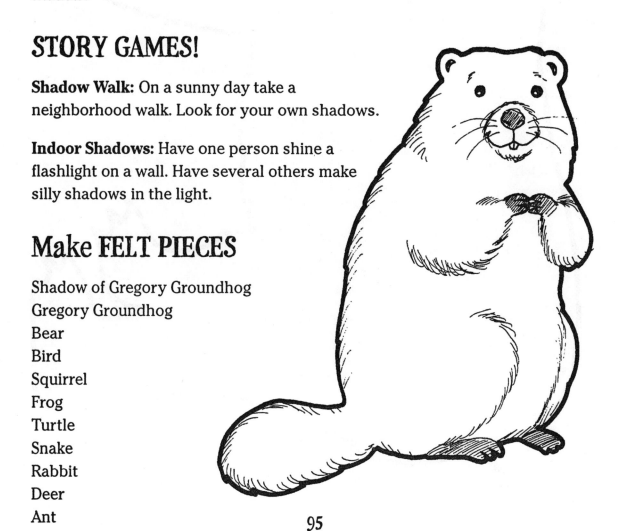

95

GREGORY GROUNDHOG LOOKS FOR HIS SHADOW

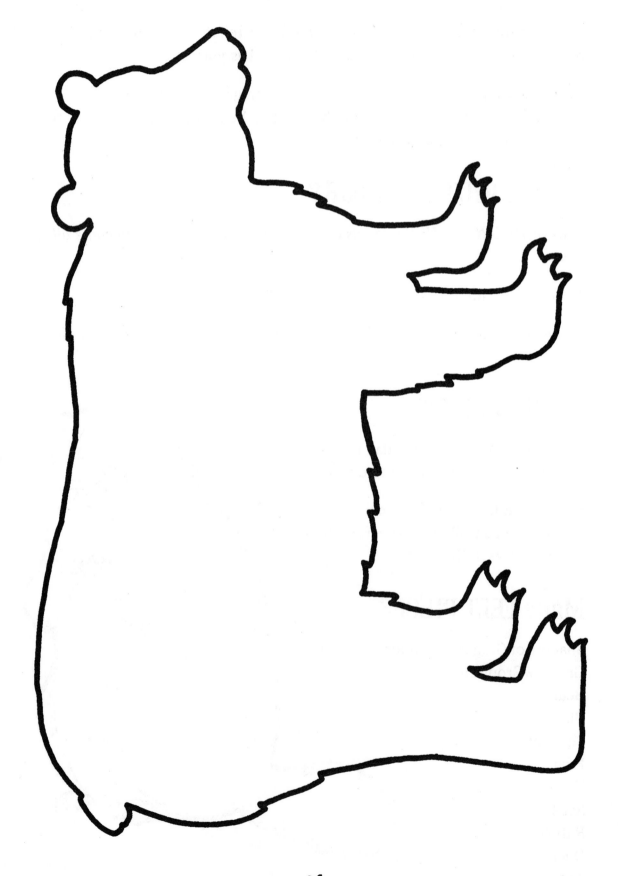

GREGORY GROUNDHOG LOOKS FOR HIS SHADOW

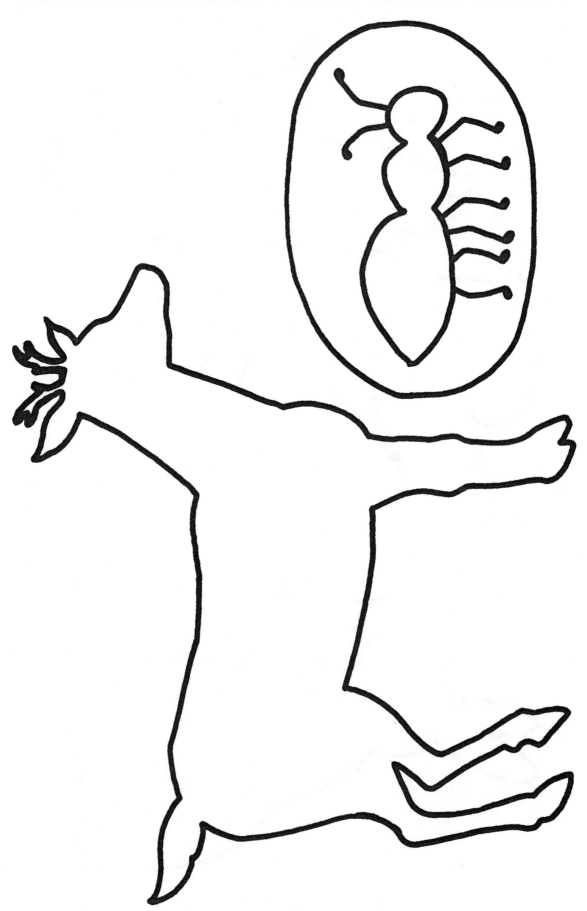

GREGORY GROUNDHOG LOOKS FOR HIS SHADOW

LET'S BUILD A BODY

(Chant and Clap Song)
by Cheryl Airhart

Chant the Refrain:

Let's build a body!
Let's build a body!
Let's put the pieces
Where they belong!

Then say, *"Let's start building our body with the HEAD."*

Repeat the refrain. Put your hands on your chest and sit up real straight as everyone chants and claps.

Then say to the children, *"What piece do you think comes next?"* (The children call out chest – stomach.) Ask, *"Who has the chest?* (Name), *please come up and put the chest under the head."*

100

Repeat the Refrain. Touch your legs as everyone chants and claps.

Say to the children, *"What do you think we should put on our body next?"* (Legs.) *"How many legs does our body need?"* (2) *"Who has the legs?* (Name) *and* (name), *you each have a leg. Please come up and add them to our body. The body is beginning to look good."*

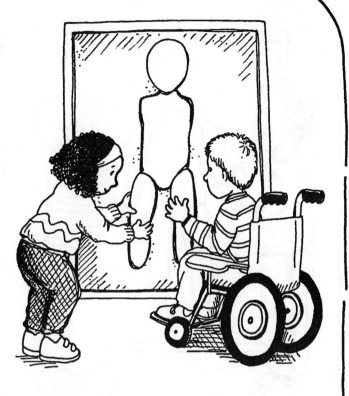

Repeat the Refrain. Touch your feet as everyone chants and claps.

Say to the children, *"I think something goes on the bottom of the legs. What do you think they are?"* (Feet.) *"How many feet does our body have?"* (2) *"You're right. We have 2 legs and at the bottom of each one is a foot. Who has the feet?* (Name) *and* (name), *you have the feet. Come up and put them on the legs."*

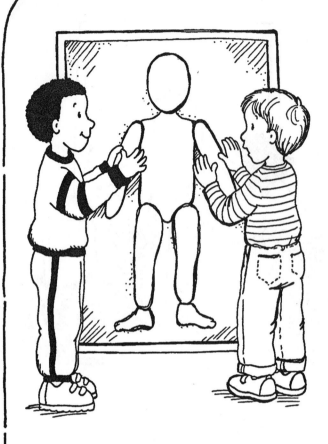

Repeat the Refrain. Wave your arms as everyone chants and claps.

Say to the children, *"It looks like the bottom half of our body is complete. What do we need on the sides of our chest?"* (Arms.) *"How many arms does our body need?"* (2) *"I bet that 2 of you have our child's arms. If you have an arm, please come up here and put it on our felt board child. Here come (name) and (name)."*

Repeat the Refrain. Move your hands around as everyone chants and claps.

Say to the children, *"We need something at the ends of our arms. What are they?"* (Hands.) *"That's right. We have 2 arms and they both need a hand. How many hands is that?"* (2) *"I know that 2 of you have the felt child's hands. Come up and put them at the ends of his arms. Thank you, (name) and (name)."*

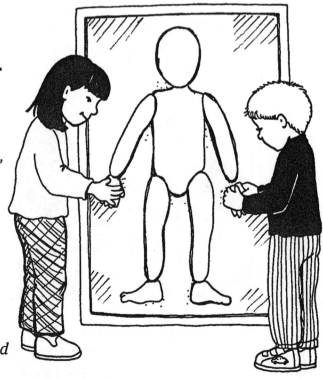

Repeat the Refrain. Touch your ears as everyone chants and claps.

Say to the children, *"Let's look at our body. Is everything there?"* (No) *"Well, what's missing?"* (Children will probably name the parts of the head.) *"You're right, we're missing the parts of the head. Let's start by putting on the child's ears. Who has the ears?* (Name) *and* (name) *come up and put the ears next to the head."*

"You also said we were missing the 2 eyes. Who has the felt child's eyes? Good. (Name) *and* (name), *please give the child some eyes. Now he can _____?"*

"Our felt child needs to smell. What does he need? Right, he needs a nose. If you have our child's nose, please come up here and give it to him. Oh thank you, (name). *Now our child can smell."*

"I think our felt child needs one more thing on his face. Does anyone have something he would like? Yes, (name) , *you have our child's mouth. Please put it under his nose."*

"His head really does need one more thing. He's got his eyes, ears, nose and mouth. What's missing?" (Hair.) *"Who has our child's hair?* (Name) *thanks for bringing it up. Put it on top of his head. What color hair does he have?"*

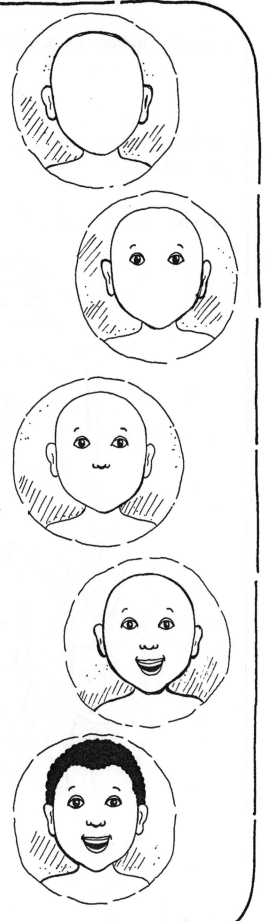

Repeat the Refrain. Touch your waist as everyone chants and claps.

After you have built your whole body say to the children, *"We have built our body, but I think something is still missing. What could it be?"* (Snowsuit) *"YES! Who has the snowsuit?"* Come up and put the child's snowsuit on."

Even more enthusiastically chant and clap the last verse!

We built a body!
We built a body!
We put the pieces
Where they belong!!!

DIRECTIONS

Pass out one or more felt piece/s to each child. You keep the head. Everyone enthusiastically chant the first verse of this Song Story. Clap as you chant.

Put the head on the top of the felt board. Repeat the refrain and then talk about the next piece you'll add to the body. (Chest.) Continue in this manner until you've built the whole body. Have fun!!

If you are telling the story to one child, let her point to each additional body part in the text or build the felt child by herself.

TALK ABOUT THE STORY

"Let's think of all the things we do with our hands." (Legs, whole body, etc.)

STORY GAMES!

Body Puzzle: Cut the pattern pieces of LET'S BUILD A BODY out of posterboard. Let your children put the body puzzle together.

Partners: Say *"hands"* and the partners touch hands together. Say *"elbows, knees, feet,"* etc. Each time partners touch.

Say and Point: Name a body part and everyone point to it.

Make FELT PIECES

(Using the felt child in his snowsuit as a guide to size, make very simple body pieces.)

Head	2 legs
Chest	2 arms
2 feet	2 ears
2 hands	Mouth
2 eyes	Hair
Nose	Snowsuit (use patterns)

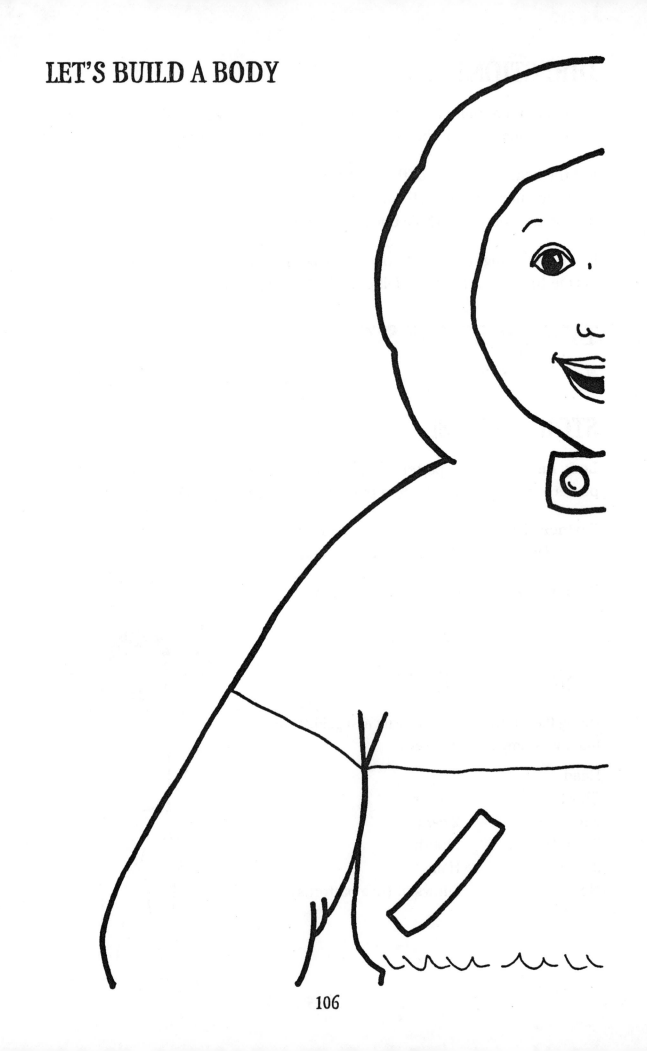

106

LET'S BUILD A BODY

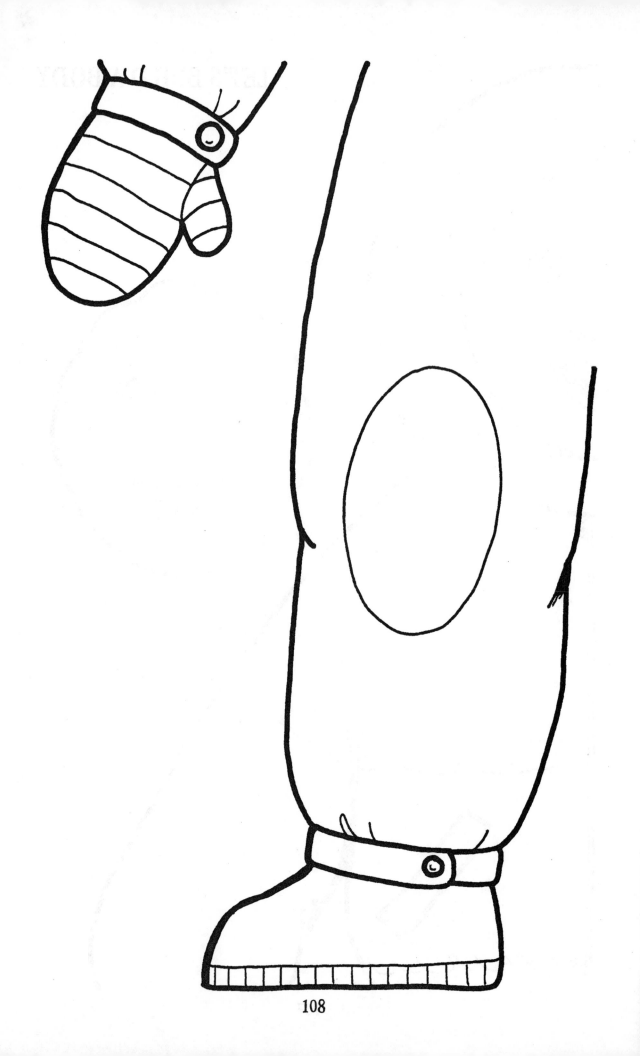

108

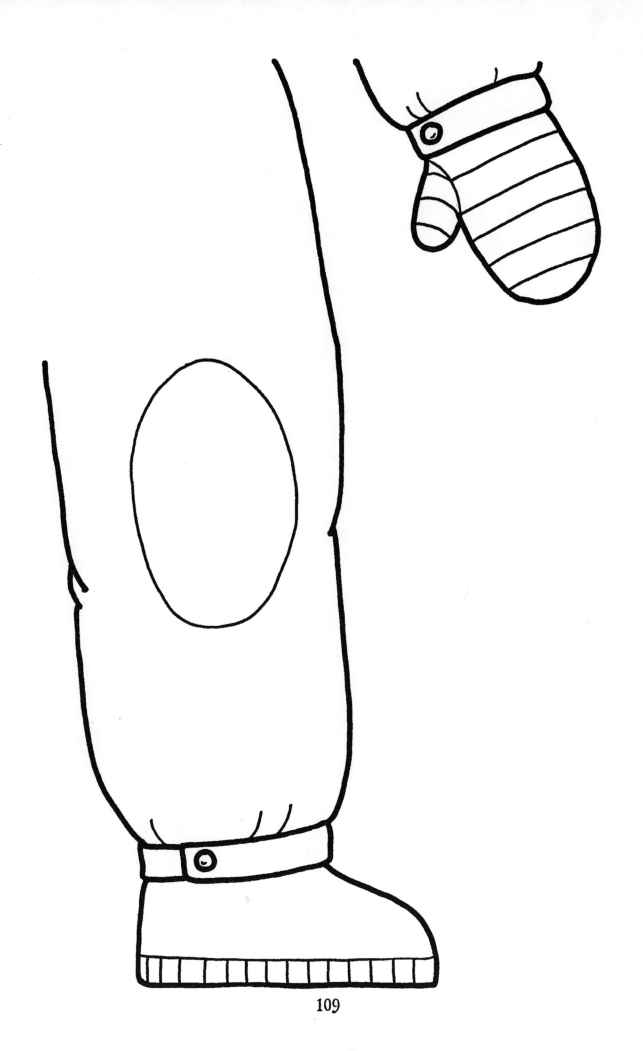

109

SPRING

FLIP-FLOP SCARECROW GETS NEW CLOTHES

Even though Flip-Flop Scarecrow was still sitting in the barn, he knew it was Springtime. He could feel the warm air, hear the rain, and smell the flowers growing around the barn.

As Flip-Flop was thinking about Spring and the cornfield he lived in, the two farm children, Kevin and Andrea, ran into the barn. As they quickly did their chores, they kept looking at Flip-Flop and giggling. They had gone through their closets and gotten all new clothes for him. Tomorrow would be the big event. The children were going to dress Flip-Flop and put him in the cornfield.

(Put Flip-Flop on the board.) When the children left, Flip-Flop started dancing from one hay bale to the next. *"Why are you so happy?"* clucked **Yellow Chicken**. *"Because Andrea and Kevin said that tomorrow I'm going to get my new clothes!"* *"What do you think you'll wear?"* whinnied **White Horse** from her stall. *"I don't know,"* said Flip-Flop. *"What do you think?"* **Pink Pig** snorted, *"I hope you wear pink sweat pants because pink is my favorite color."* (Put sweat pants on Flip-Flop.)

"I hope you get a new belt," whinnied **White Horse**. (Put belt on Flip-Flop.) *"Last year you had a blue one made from some old yarn. Your pants were always falling down. Maybe this year you'll get some of that bright green clothesline."* "Oh, I hope so," said Flip-Flop. *"That would be great with pink sweat pants."*

(Put striped shirt, then the checked shirt on Flip-Flop.) **White Horse** said, *"When I was out in the yard, I saw Andrea holding up a big striped shirt and Kevin was holding a checked one. Maybe you'll get one of those."* Flip-Flop was so happy. He said, *"That would be great. I saw Farmer Klein wearing the checked shirt last year. I liked the red and yellow colors."*

Yellow Chicken reminded Flip-Flop that his old work gloves were full of holes and he would need a new pair. *"I remember,"* said Flip Flop. *"I could hardly do any work by the end of last year."* (Put gloves on Flip-Flop.)

(Try different hats on Flip-Flop.) *"I wonder what your hat will look like?"* asked **Pink Pig**. *"Maybe you will have a construction hat or a firefighter's helmet,"* whinnied **White Horse**. *"Sometimes those big birds get very close."* *"I have a better idea,"* clucked **Yellow Chicken**. *"Mrs. Klein's wide straw hat would be perfect. It would keep the hot sun off your skin, Flip-Flop."* *"You're right Yellow Chicken,"* said Flip-Flop, *"but I wouldn't be able to see very well. The brim would get in my way."* **Pink Pig** oinked, *"Well, maybe you need a top hat like Frosty."* *"I'm afraid that it would blow away,"* said Flip-Flop. *"I guess we'll just have to see what the children bring me."*

Flip-Flop could only think about his new clothes. As it got dark, he closed his eyes and began dreaming of himself in a checked shirt, with pink sweat pants held up by a green rope tied tightly around his waist. He was proud of his new gloves. But what kind of hat? He saw himself in a baseball cap, a swimming cap, and a straw hat. As he turned over in his bed, he decided that he would just have to wait until tomorrow to see what hat the children had picked out for him.

**Good night.
Happy dreams everyone!**

DIRECTIONS

Put Flip-Flop on the felt board. Read the story. As you do, dress Flip-Flop in his new clothes. Try on different shirts. Put different hats on his head. Let the children decide which one they like best.

TALK ABOUT THE STORY

"If you were dressing Flip-Flop, what clothes would you put on him?"

"Do you like getting new clothes? Where do you get your clothes?"

"If you were Flip-Flop what hat would you like to wear?"

STORY GAMES

What Hat Should I Wear: Put several hats on a table near a full length mirror. Encourage the children to pretend they are Flip-Flop as they try them on. What do they like best?

Make FELT PIECES

Flip-Flop dancing
Pink sweat pants
Green clothesline belt
Striped shirt
Checked shirt
Work gloves
Construction hat
Firefighter helmet
Straw hat
Baseball hat
Swim cap
Top hat

FLIP-FLOP SCARECROW GETS NEW CLOTHES

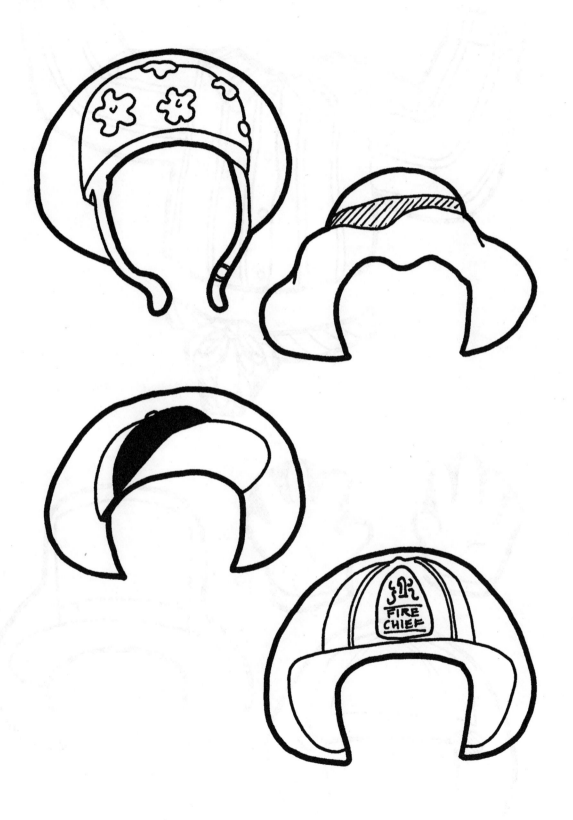

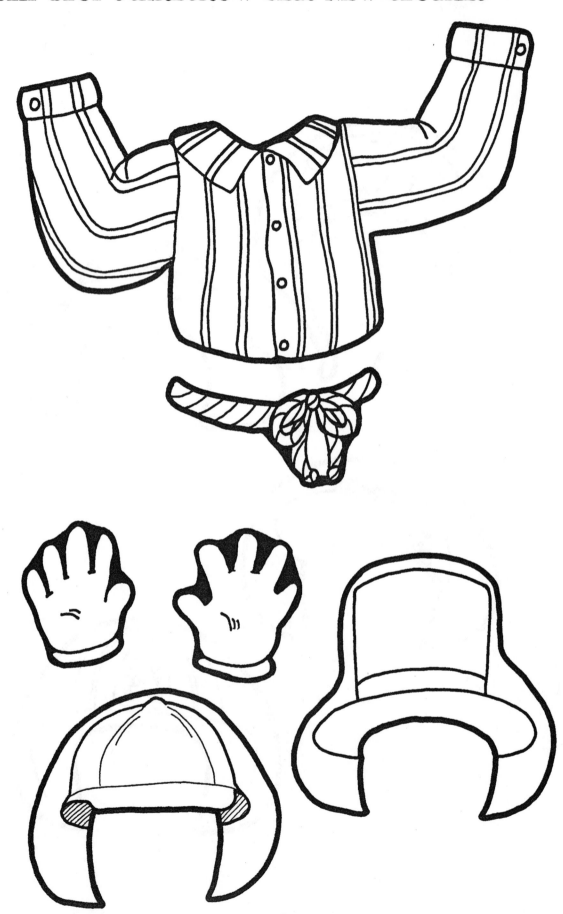

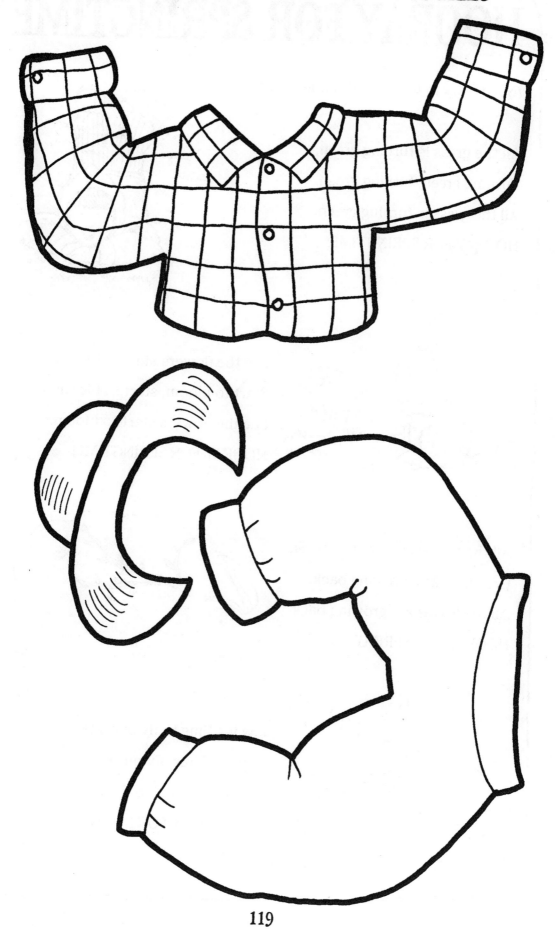

HOORAY FOR SPRINGTIME

(Song Story to the tune of Mulberry Bush)

All the grass is turning green,
Turning green, turning green.
All the grass is turning green.
HOORAY FOR SPRINGTIME!

See the flowers start to bloom,
Start to bloom, start to bloom.
See the flowers start to bloom.
HOORAY FOR SPRINGTIME!

All the leaves are growing back,
Growing back, growing back.
All the leaves are growing back.
HOORAY FOR SPRINGTIME!

Now it's time to fly our kites,
Fly our kites, fly our kites.
Now it's time to fly our kites.
HOORAY FOR SPRINGTIME!

See the birds build their nests,
Build their nests, build their nests.
See the birds build their nests.
HOORAY FOR SPRINGTIME!

Feel the rain on our arms,
On our arms, on our arms.
Feel the rain on our arms.
HOORAY FOR SPRINGTIME!

Watch the worms twist and wiggle,
Twist and wiggle, twist and wiggle.
Watch the worms twist and wiggle.
HOORAY FOR SPRINGTIME!

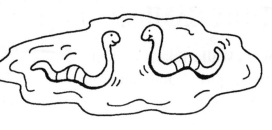

Yellow dandelions pop right up,
Pop right up, pop right up.
Yellow dandelions pop right up.
HOORAY FOR SPRINGTIME!

Listen to thunder snap and crack,
Snap and crack, snap and crack.
Listen to thunder snap and crack.
HOORAY FOR SPRINGTIME!

DIRECTIONS

Sing the Song Story. Put the felt pieces on the board as you sing each verse.

TALK ABOUT THE STORY

Name other signs of Spring, such as caterpillars, lightning, raincoats, umbrellas, etc. Make up more verses. Next time you sing, substitute your verses for some of the existing ones.

Example:

Hold the umbrella over your head,
Over your head, over your head.
Hold the umbrella over your head.
HOORAY FOR SPRINGTIME!

STORY GAMES!

Spring Walk: Take a walk in your neighborhood and look for the signs of Spring.

Fly a Kite: On a warm day take a plastic grocery bag outside. Hold onto the handles and fly it like a kite.

Make FELT PIECES

Green grass	Several flowers
Tree with leaves	Kite
Nest	Bird
Raindrop	Worm
Dandelion	Thunder

HOORAY FOR SPRINGTIME

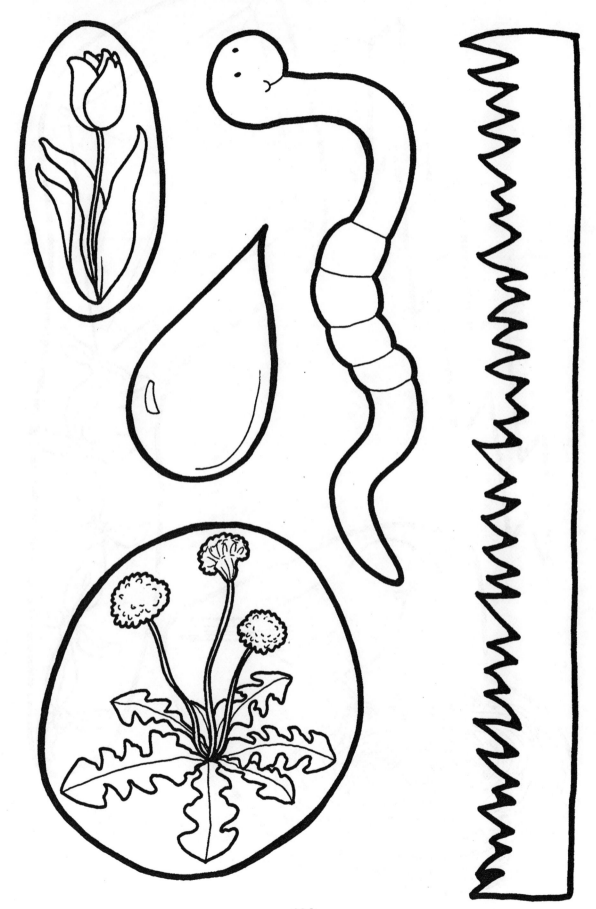

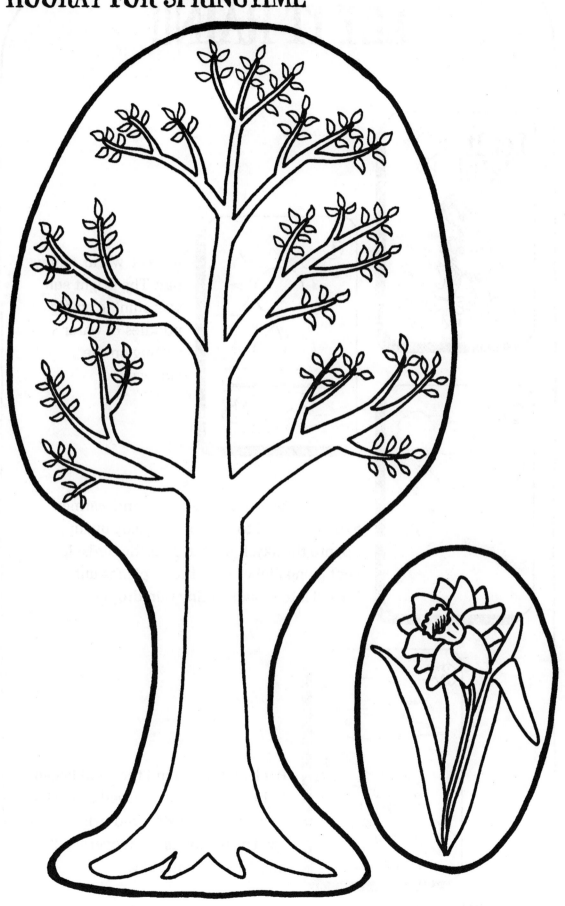

LET IT RAIN!!

by Jane Flynn

It was a warm, sunny day. The bright sun was shining on big puddles of water resting on the sidewalk.

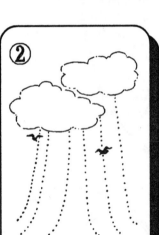

The water was getting warmer and warmer. Soon it started to evaporate, going up, up, up into the sky. It floated past the birds. It kept going higher than the airplanes until it turned into clouds of tiny rain droplets.

Back on the ground the wind began to blow. The trees swayed from side to side and the kites did twirls in the air. Those clouds, high overhead, moved across the sky.

Soon the tiny rain droplets gathered together into bigger drops and formed dark clouds. They were so heavy. They asked each other, *"What should we do? We are so heavy! We can't stay here."*

Finally they had a brilliant idea. They all looked at each other and said, *"LET IT RAIN!"*

At once they became raindrops and started falling from the sky. They landed on the flowers and trees, the fields and forests, the rooftops and the children, plus the worms, squirrels and birds. Lots of water fell on the roads, sidewalks, and parking lots. The rain drops joined together to make big and small puddles.

The RAINDROPS had worked very hard. They had evaporated, climbed into the sky, floated along in the clouds, and then tumbled back down to the earth. They were all sooooo tired. They fell asleep in their puddles, on the leaves, in the grass, and on top of umbrellas. They stayed sound asleep until that big bright sun came up again and started to carry them back to the sky to join the clouds and rain all over again.

DIRECTIONS

Tell the children this Sequence Story of RAIN. Put the Rain Cards on the felt board as the story develops.

TALK ABOUT THE STORY

"What do you like best about the rain? Least?"

"Did you ever get caught in a rainstorm? What did you do?"

STORY GAMES

Puddle Walk: One day, after it has rained, take a walk around your neighborhood and look for puddles. Are they big or small?

Rain Rhymes: See pages 132-133.

Making Puddles: Put a sprinkling can filled with water in the sand pile. Encourage children to make their own puddles.

Make FELT PIECES

7 story cards

LET IT RAIN!

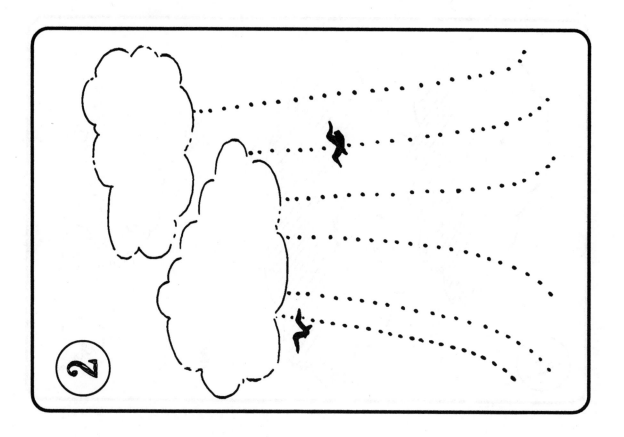

LET IT RAIN!

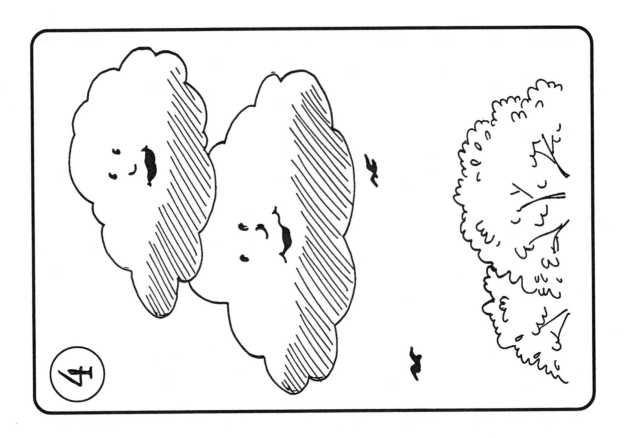

LET IT RAIN!

LET IT RAIN!

Enjoy these
fingerplays
after enjoying
LET IT RAIN!

Rainy Day Fun

Slip on your raincoat.

Pull up your galoshes.

Wade in puddles.

Make splishes and sploshes.

Raindrops

Rain on the green grass.

Rain on the trees.

Rain on the housetops.

But not on me.

SPLISH – SPLASH

Finally the rain stopped. Liz and Dick were so excited. Now they could go outside and SPLISH-SPLASH in all the puddles. They put on their rain coats and boots and ran out the door.

The twins ran to the first puddle they saw and jumped right in – SPLISH! Liz watched the water fly into the air and land back on the sidewalk. She stared at the new puddle and said, *"Dick, Dick, I made a _____ ."*

Dick jumped in the big puddle – SPLASH! *"Look Liz, I made a _____ !"*

"Let's see what else we can make." SPLISH went Liz. *"It's a _____ ."*

SPLASH went Dick. *"It's a _____ . RRRRRRR!"*

Liz yelled, *"There's another puddle! Let's jump in it. We'll hold hands and do it together."* SPLISH-SPLASH. *"Look Dick,"* said Liz, *"We made a _____! That's so funny, a whale swimming in a puddle in front of our house."*

"This is so much fun," said Dick. *"What else can we SPLISH-SPLASH? I know, I'll close my eyes and jump. You tell me what I made."* SPLISH – *"You made a _____, Dick. My turn,"* said Liz.

SPLASH – *"Oh Liz, you made the _____. Now the puddles are twins just like us."*

Liz called out to Dick, *"It looks like it's going to rain again. Let's SPLISH-SPLASH as fast as we can and see what else we can make before it rains. You go first, Dick."*

SPLISH – *"It's a _____."*

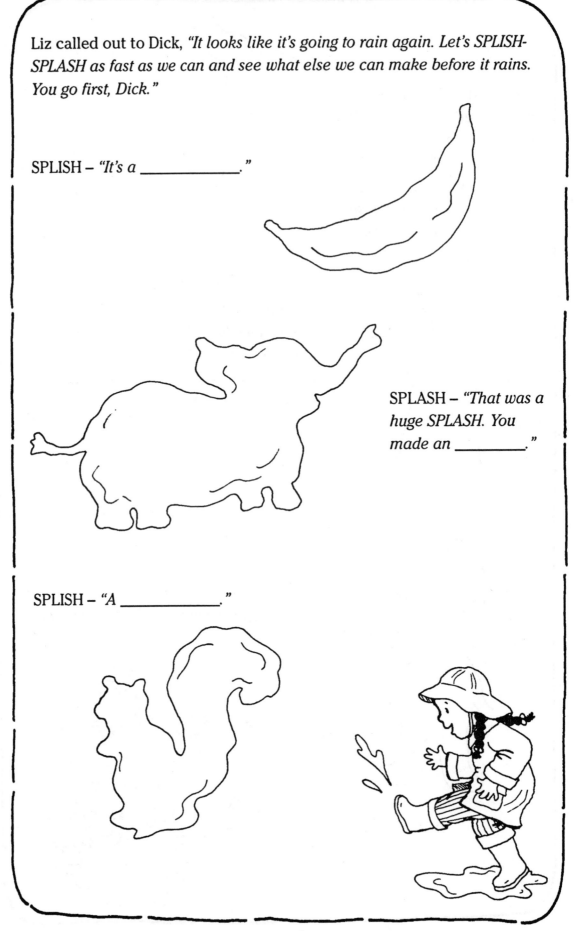

SPLASH – *"That was a huge SPLASH. You made an _____."*

SPLISH – *"A _____."*

SPLASH – "A _____."

SPLISH – "A _____."

SPLASH – "You splashed a _____."

"Oh Liz, mom is waving at us to come inside. Let's SPLISH-SPLASH as we run to the house."

SPLISH – What did Dick make? (Let the children decide.)

SPLASH – What did Liz make? (Let the children decide.)

DIRECTIONS

Read the story. As you read each SPLISH and SPLASH, put the shape on the felt board or point to the picture. Let the children call out each SPLISH and SPLASH.

TALK ABOUT THE STORY

"What other SPLISHES-SPLASHES do you think the twins could have made?"

"Have you ever played SPLISH-SPLASH? What shapes did you see in your puddles?"

STORY GAMES!

Outside SPLISH-SPLASH: After the next rain in your neighborhood, go outside and play SPLISH-SPLASH.

Look At the Clouds: On a warm, cloudy day look up in the sky. Pick a cloud. Do you see any shapes in it? What? Pick another cloud and find more shapes. Did you see a giraffe? Bear? Shovel? Tree?

Make FELT PIECES

Tree

Boat

Whale

Gingerbread girl

Elephant

Star

Dog

Bear

Lion

Gingerbread boy

Banana

Squirrel

Birthday cake

SPLISH-SPLASH

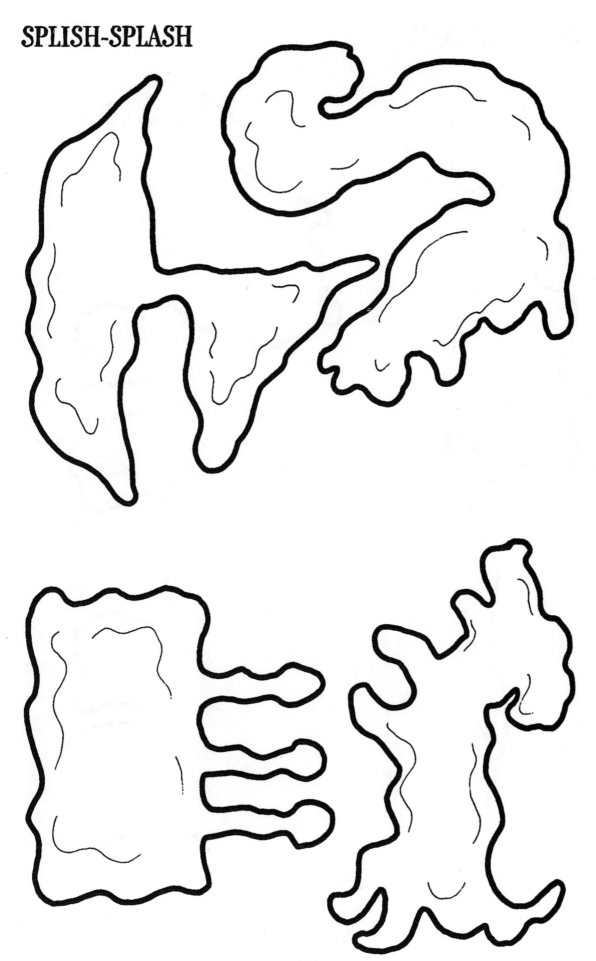

SPLISH-SPLASH

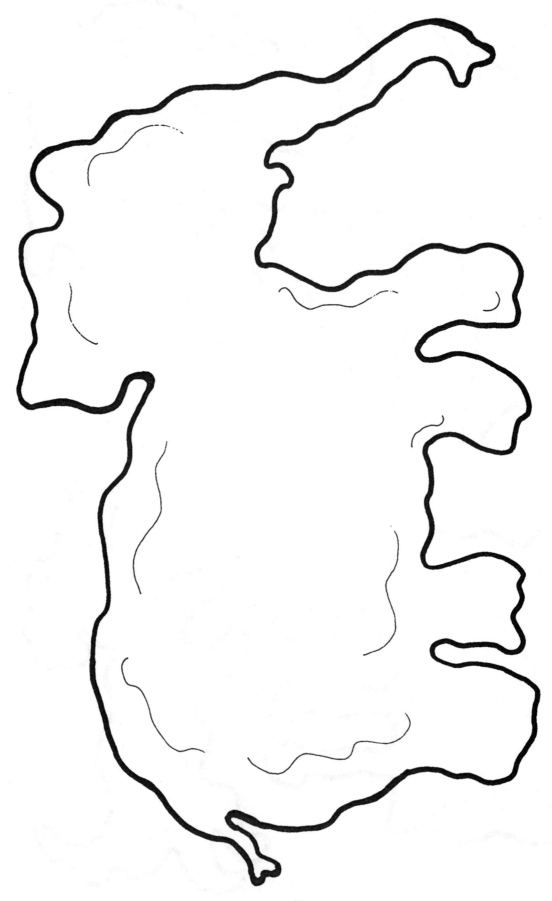

SPLISH-SPLASH

SPLISH-SPLASH

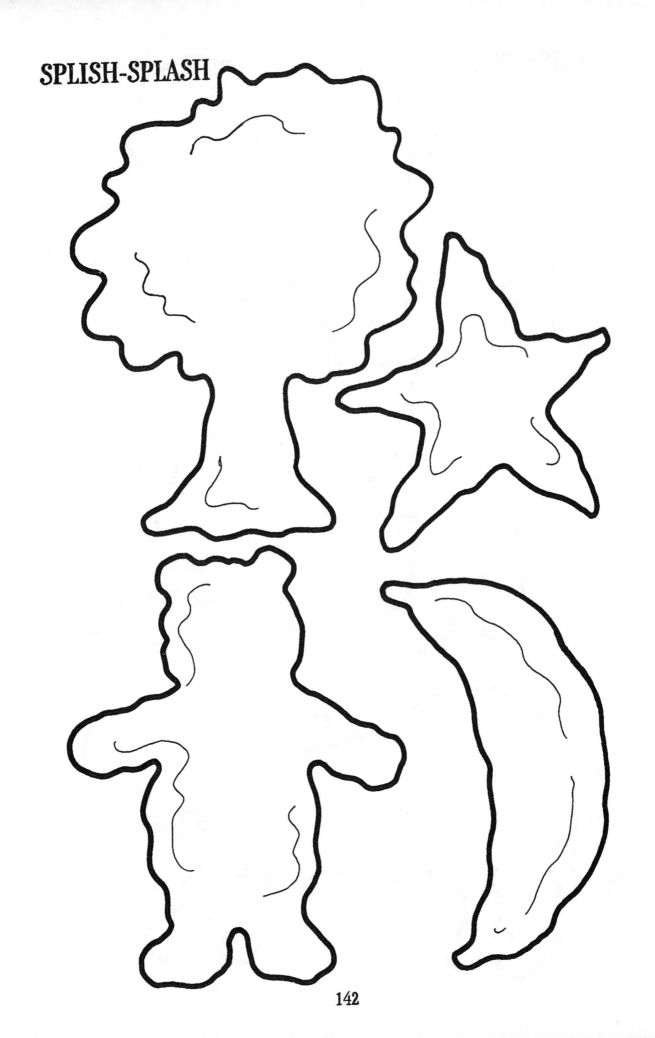

SPLISH-SPLASH

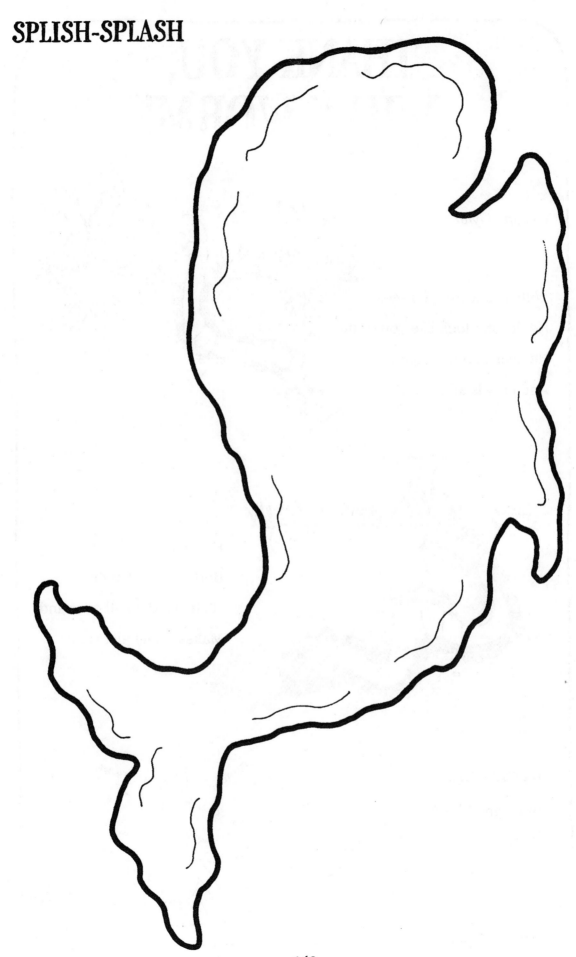

THANK YOU, WILLY WORM!

by Jane Flynn

Willy is a worm you see.

He doesn't look like you or me.

He lives in the ground,

And crawls all around.

He works very hard,

Both day and night.

He turns the soil over and

Makes it feel just right.

He has no teeth,

But a great big tummy.

He thinks leaves and roots

Are real, real yummy!

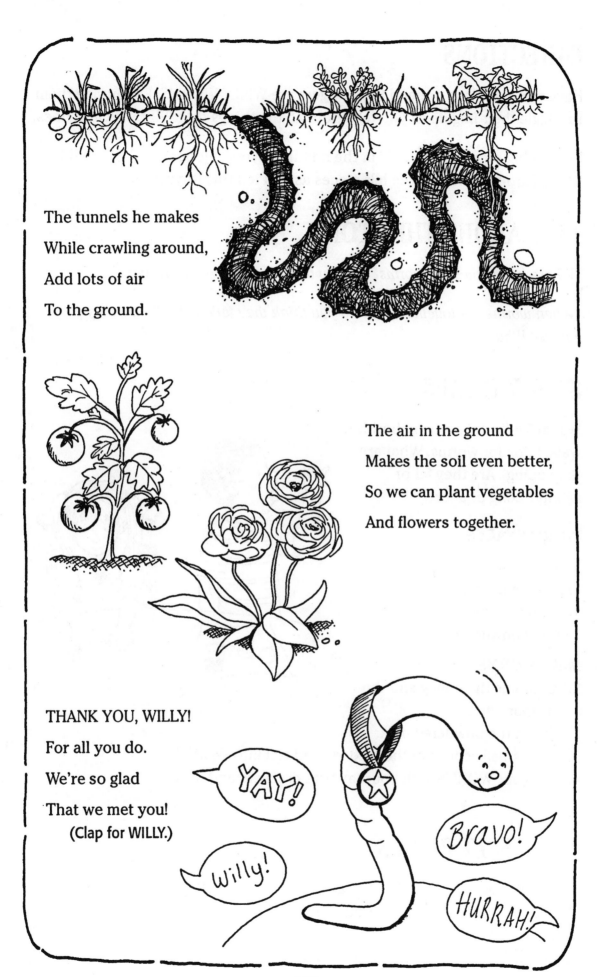

The tunnels he makes
While crawling around,
Add lots of air
To the ground.

The air in the ground
Makes the soil even better,
So we can plant vegetables
And flowers together.

THANK YOU, WILLY!
For all you do.
We're so glad
That we met you!
 (Clap for WILLY.)

YAY!

Willy!

Bravo!

HURRAH!

145

DIRECTIONS

Have your children pretend their fingers are WILLY WORMS. Encourage them to wiggle their fingers as you tell about all the things that WILLY WORM does.

Put the big piece of "ground" in the middle of your felt board. Wiggle WILLY WORM around and add the felt pieces as you tell this Rhyme Story.

TALK ABOUT THE STORY

"Where have you seen worms? Do you think any of them were WILLY?"

"When worms are together what do you think they talk about?" "Do they play games? What?"

STORY GAMES!

Worm Walk: Take a neighborhhod walk. Look for worms. What are they doing? Are they fat or skinny? Long or short?

WORM SNACKS

You'll Need
1/2 cup of peanut butter
1/2 cup of honey
1 cup of powdered milk

Make WORMS
1. Combine the honey and the peanut butter.
2. Stir in the powdered milk.
3. Take small scoops of the mixture and roll into WORMS.
4. Eat your WORMS with your favorite crackers and milk.

Make FELT PIECES

WILLY WORM	Leaf	Root
Tunnel	Flowers	Vegetables

WILLY WORM taking a bow
Large patch of dirt (Cut a large piece of black felt.)

THANK YOU, WILLY WORM

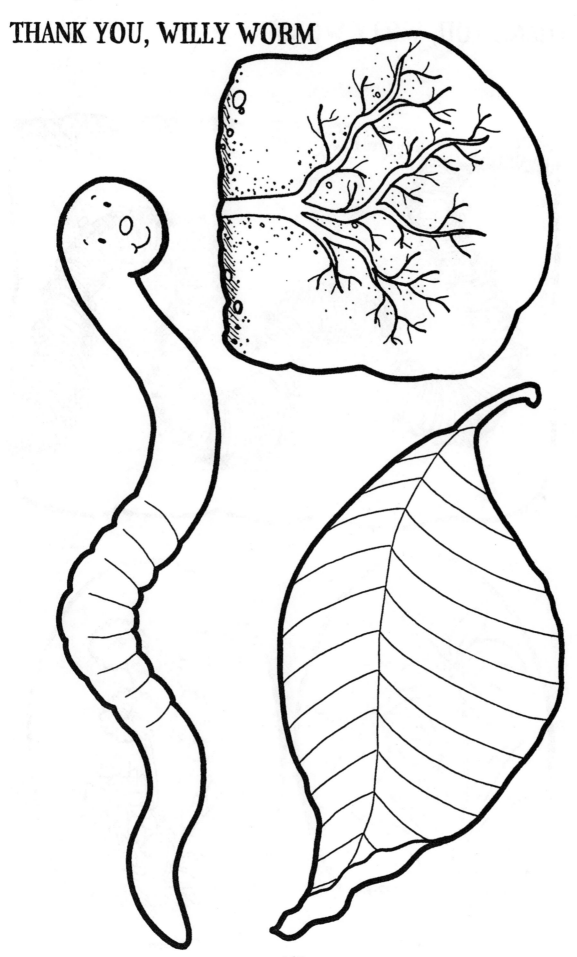

THANK YOU, WILLY WORM

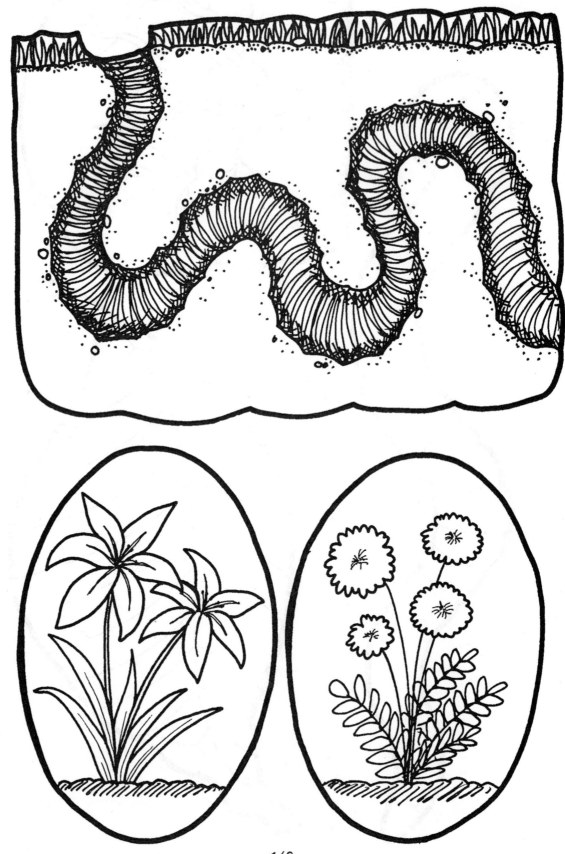

THANK YOU, WILLY WORM

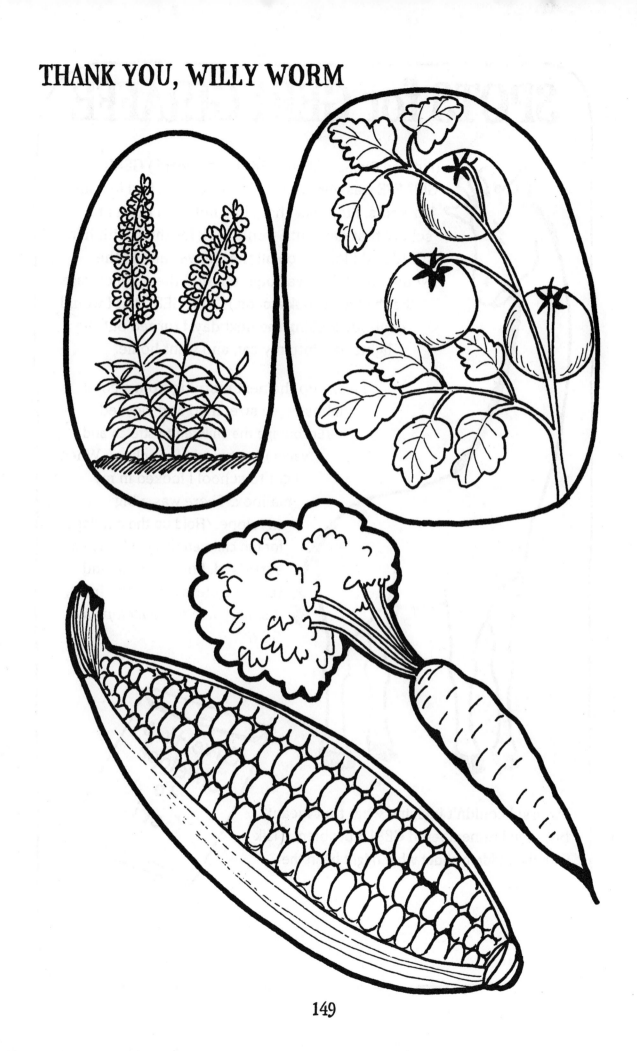

SPOTS for GERI GIRAFFE

(Put Geri Giraffe without spots on the board.) GERI GIRAFFE was very upset. Somehow she had lost all her spots. I told her that I had not seen them in school that day, but I would look for them with her. GERI and I looked on all the shelves and in the containers, but we could not find them. (Encourage the children to look around.) I told GERI that I would continue looking the next day. I turned out the lights, got into my car, and went home.

I woke up the next morning from a good night sleep. I stretched and yawned. (Encourage the children to stretch and yawn.) I got ready for school. When I got to school I looked in my mailbox. There was a big envelope. (Hold up the envelope for the children to see.) I was so surprised. I picked it up and read the message on the front. It said, *"Give this envelope to GERI."*

At first I couldn't imagine what that meant, but then I remembered GERI'S problem. (Talk with the children about what might be in the envelope.)

Give this envelope to Geri.

I rushed into school with the envelope. I walked right up to GERI and said to her, *"Look what I found on the front seat of my car this morning. It is an envelope addressed to you. Can I open it for you?"* Excitedly GERI said, *"Yes! Yes!"* I opened the envelope, looked inside and said to GERI, *"You'll be so happy, but you'll also be very surprised."* (Open the envelope and slowly pull out one spot. Ask the children what color and/or shape the spot is. Put it on GERI. Continue pulling out the spots, naming the colors and/or shapes, and adding each one to GERI.)

(After Geri has all of her spots back, ask her.) *"Well GERI what do you think of your new spots?"* She was so excited, that all she could say was, *"Thank you, I love my new colors. I'll look so bright and cheerful when I walk around the room. The children will love me as I talk and play with them. Do you think they will like my new spots?"* (Let the children call out an answer.)

151

DIRECTIONS

Put all the felt colored spots in a big envelope. Write on the front of the envelope, *"Give this envelope to GERI GIRAFFE."*

Put GERI GIRAFFE on the felt board. Tell the children that GERI is a friend of yours who has decided to live at school. Yesterday when you were leaving, GERI stopped you. She had a problem.

Tell this story as if you were the teacher helping GERI find her spots.

TALK ABOUT THE STORY

"Have you ever lost anything? What was it? Did you find it? Where? How did you feel when you found the lost item?"

STORY GAMES

My Spots: Have lots of removable sticker dots and figures. Let the children put stickers on their arms and pretend they are GERI GIRAFFE.

GERI GIRAFFE Visits Our Room:
Cut out a large GERI GIRAFFE from posterboard. Have lots of stickers. Let the children give GERI her "spots" back. Hang her in the book area.

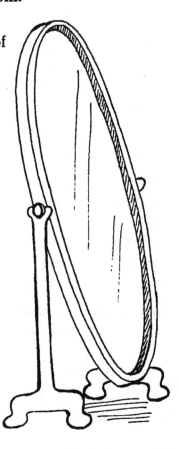

Make FELT PIECES

Large giraffe without spots
Red heart
Blue star
Green shamrock
Black hat
Brown leaf
Yellow moon
White egg
Purple kite
Orange pumpkin
Pink flower

SPOTS FOR GERI GIRAFFE

SPOTS FOR GERI GIRAFFE

SPOTS FOR GERI GIRAFFE

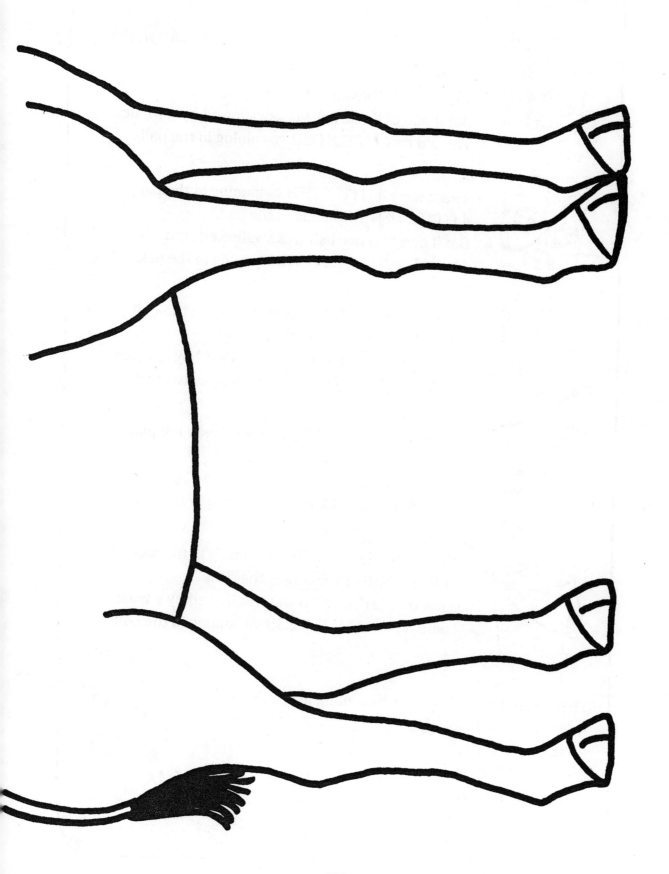

WHALE AND THE FISH

by Cheryl Airhart

There were 5 LITTLE FISH swimming in the pail,
5 LITTLE FISH swimming in the pail.
But if one of those fish was swallowed by a whale,
There'd be 4 LITTLE FISH swimming in the pail.

There were 4 LITTLE FISH swimming in the pail,
4 LITTLE FISH swimming in the pail.
But if one of those fish was swallowed by a whale,
There'd be 3 LITTLE FISH swimming in the pail.

There were 3 LITTLE FISH swimming in the pail,
3 LITTLE FISH swimming in the pail.
But if one of those fish was swallowed by a whale,
There'd be 2 LITTLE FISH swimming in the pail.

There were 2 LITTLE FISH swimming in the pail.
2 LITTLE FISH swimming in the pail.
But if one of those fish was swallowed by a whale,
There'd be 1 LITTLE FISH swimming in the pail.

There was 1 LITTLE FISH swimming in the pail.
1 LITTLE FISH swimming in the pail.
But if that LITTLE FISH was swallowed by a whale,
There'd be NO LITTLE FISH swimming in the pail.

There were NO LITTLE FISH swimming in the pail.
No little fish swimming in
    the pail.
But if ALL 5 FISH were spit
    back by the whale,
There'd be 5 LITTLE FISH
    swimming the pail.

DIRECTIONS

Put the pail and the fish on the felt board. Put the whale nearby. Chant this Number Story with the children.

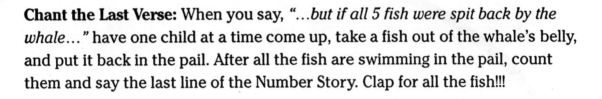

Start Chanting: As you say, *'But if one…'* take one fish off the pail, give it to a child and have him feed it to the whale. Count the 4 fish that are still swimming in the pail and then chant the verse. Let another child feed a fish to the whale. Continue until there are no fish swimming in the pail.

Chant the Last Verse: When you say, *"…but if all 5 fish were spit back by the whale…"* have one child at a time come up, take a fish out of the whale's belly, and put it back in the pail. After all the fish are swimming in the pail, count them and say the last line of the Number Story. Clap for all the fish!!!

TALK ABOUT THE STORY

"How big do you think that whale in our story really was? As big as a car?"

"If you were a fish swimming in the ocean, where could you hide if you saw whale coming?"

Make FELT PIECES

Pail
5 fish
Big whale

STORY GAMES!

Different Ending: Bring back one fish at a time instead of all 5 fish at once. Continue the rhyme as follows.

There were NO LITTLE FISH swimming in the pail.
No little fish swimming in the pail.
But if 1 LITTLE FISH was spit back by the whale,
There'd be 1 LITTLE FISH swimming in the pail.

There was 1 LITTLE FISH swimming in the pail.
1 LITTLE FISH swimming in the pail.
But if 1 MORE FISH was spit back by the whale,
There'd be 2 LITTLE FISH swimming in the pail.

Continue until all 5 fish are back in the pail.

157

WHALE AND THE FISH

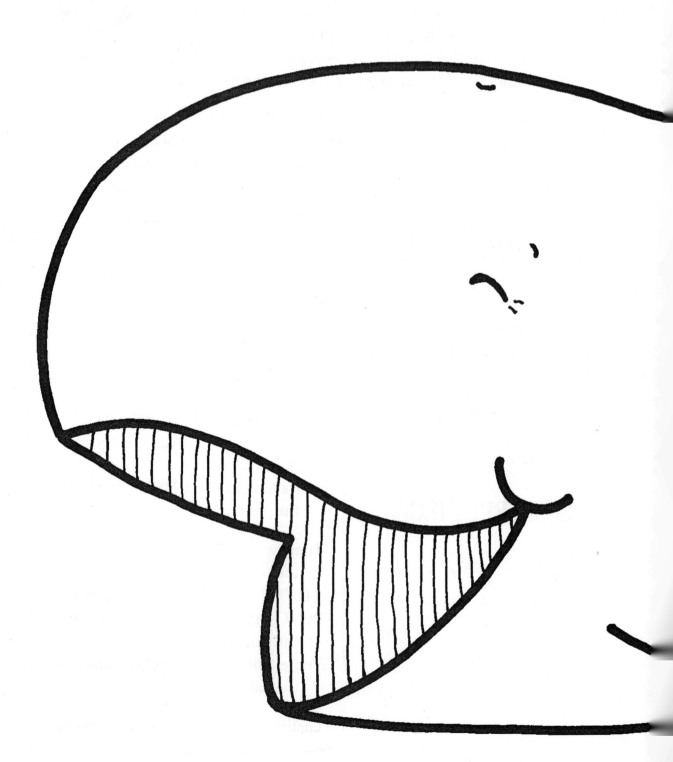

WHALE AND THE FISH

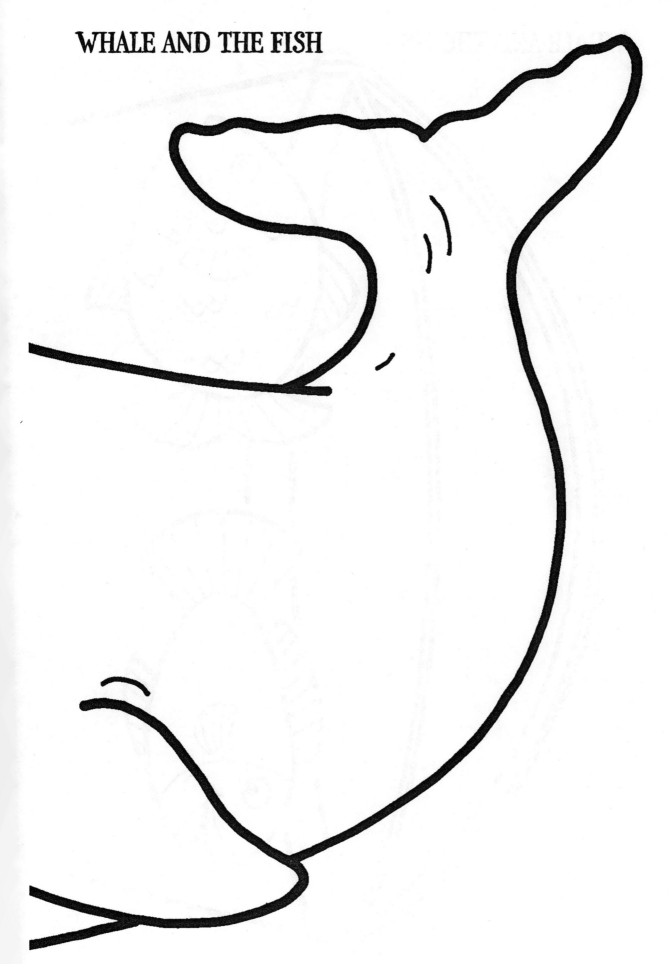

WHALE AND THE FISH

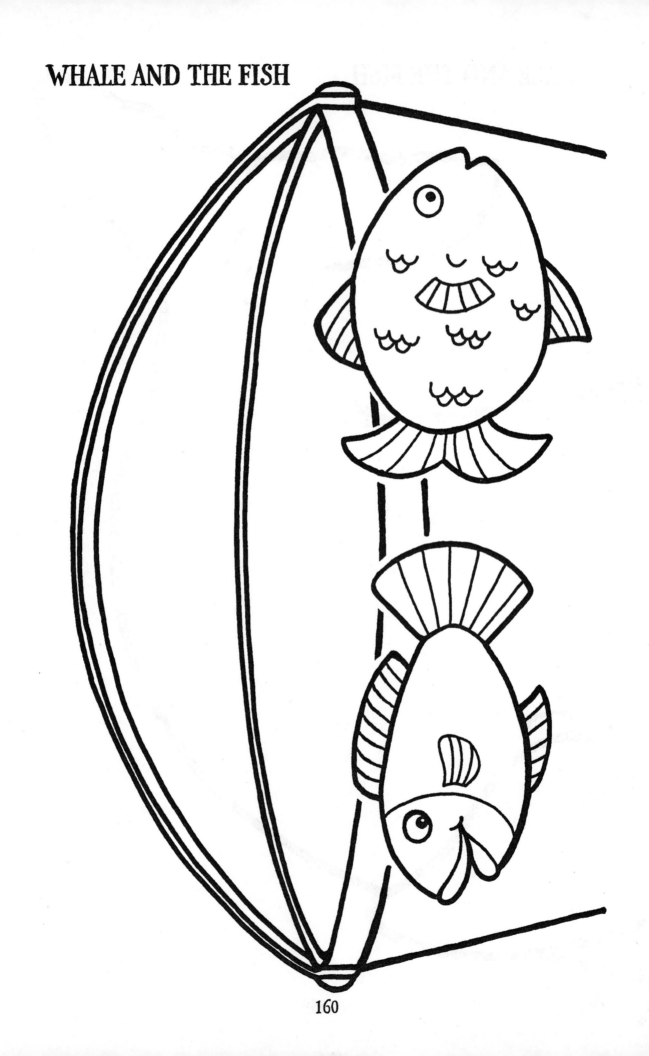

WHALE AND THE FISH

SUMMER

FLIP-FLOP GOES TO THE BIRTHDAY PARTY

(Put Flip-Flip on board.) Flip-Flop Scarecrow had been standing high on his pole all day, keeping the crows out of Farmer Klein's cornfield. (Put butterfly next to Flip-Flop's ear.) In the late afternoon, a butterfly quietly flew over to Flip-Flop and whispered in his ear, *"Tonight is Patchwork Scarecrow's birthday party. All the scarecrows are getting together in Patchwork's cornfield. Dapple, the old gray horse, will pick you up in the hay wagon."*

Flip-Flop was so happy. He loved seeing friends. Finally the sun went down and the crows went to sleep in the trees. (Put Dapple and wagon on board.) Flip-Flop heard Dapple coming. (Put birthday hat on Flip-Flop.) Flip-Flop put on his birthday hat and climbed into the hay wagon.

(Put stars and moon on board.) The stars and moon lit up the fields as Dapple trotted along to pick up the other scarecrows. Soon they were on their way to Patchwork's birthday party. As Dapple trotted under the bright sky, the six scarecrows laughed as they rolled around the wagon bumping into each other and tumbling into the hay bales. They tossed hay high in the air while singing their favorite scarecrow songs. Here's one of them. Sing it with them. (Let the children sing.)

WHEN THE CROWS BEGIN TO FLY

(tune: When the Saints Go Marching In)

by Dick Wilmes

When the crows begin to fly,
Oh when the crows begin to fly.
I want to be in that cornfield,
When the crows begin to fly.

When the sun begins to shine...

When the wind begins to blow...

When the rain begins to pour...

Add your own verses.

Last Verse:

BUT...
When the snow begins to fall,
When the snow begins to fall.
Please put me in the red barn,
When the snow begins to fall.

(Put Patchwork on board.) Finally Dapple and the scarecrows arrived at Patchwork's field. When Patchwork saw Dapple bringing her scarecrow friends, she called out, *"Oh I'm so glad to see you. Let's play Dance Round the Corn Stalks. It is my favorite birthday game."* The scarecrows jumped off the hay wagon and joined hands in a big circle. They started singing and dancing. (Hold hands and form a circle. Sing and dance with the scarecrows as you move in a circle.)

DANCE ROUND THE CORNSTALKS

(tune: Mulberry Bush)
by Liz Wilmes

Let's dance round the corn stalks,
The corn stalks, the corn stalks.
Let's dance round the corn stalks,
At Patchwork's birthday party.

(Dance the other way and sing again.)

After awhile Haystack yelled, *"Let's play Corn Stalk Jump"* "Yes! Yes!" yelled all the scarecrows as they each jumped onto a corn stalk. Haystack called out, *"1, 2, 3 GO!"* and the scarecrows jumped from corn stalk to corn stalk until they reached the end of the field. *"That was fun. Let's jump back,"* called Patchwork.

(Put birthday cake on board.) When they all got back, Patchwork's brother and sister were bringing out the birthday cake. Everyone clapped and sang "Happy Birthday" to Patchwork." She made a wish and blew out all her candles. The scarecrows each had a big piece of cake with ice cream and a juicy red cherry on top. Delicious!

"Let's play another game," called Haystack. "How about Climb the Corn Stalks?" "Good idea," they all yelled. All the scarecrows stood at the bottom of a corn stalk. Once again Haystack said, "1, 2, 3 GO!" The scarecrows started to climb their corn stalks as fast as they could. As they got to the top, each one yelled, "I'm on top!"

They looked all around. They could see the stars and moon. Not too far away fireflies flashed signals to each other. (Put bullfrog on board.) "Listen," said Haystack "I can hear the bullfrogs singing Happy Birthday to Patchwork." (Put crow on board.) Flip-Flop pointed to the trees near the edge of the field and said, "Look friends, the crows are waking up and flying out of the trees. Soon they will be in our cornfields. We must get back to work!"

Thank you for coming!

The scarecrows scurried down the corn stalks and thanked Patchwork for inviting them to her birthday party. They jumped into the hay wagon. As Dapple trotted away, all the scarecrows waved "good-bye" and sang HAPPY BIRTHDAY to Patchwork one more time. (Sing Happy Birthday.)

DIRECTIONS

Read the story. As you do, put the felt pieces on the board.

TALK ABOUT THE STORY

"What do you do when you go to a birthday party? Do you do the same things as Flip-Flop and his friends?"

"What do you eat at birthday parties? Is that what Flip-Flop and his friends ate?"

"Tell me about your birthday."

STORY GAMES

Pretend Birthday: Get out the birthday hats. Wear them at lunch. Sing Happy Birthday to everyone.

Birthday Games: Play:
- London Bridges
- Ring Around the Rosie
- Follow the Leader
- Others you think of

Make FELT PIECES

Flip-Flop on his pole
Horse pulling wagon
Flip-Flop with birthday hat
   (Use the pattern of Flip-Flop on his pole.
   Add a birthday hat.)

Stars	Several Crows	Butterfly
Patchwork	Birthday cake	Moon
Bull frog		

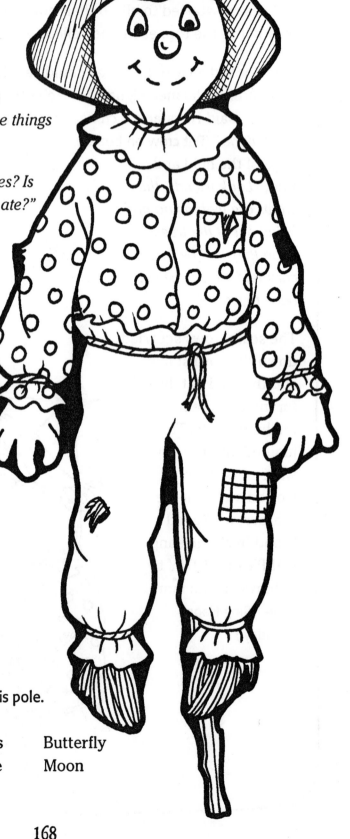

FLIP-FLOP GOES TO THE BIRTHDAY PARTY

FLIP-FLOP GOES TO THE BIRTHDAY PARTY

PICNIC ON THE MOON

Flip-Flop Scarecrow was waiting for the sun to set over the cornfield. During the day he had made plans with Andrea and Kevin, the two farm children, to visit Moon.

(Put Moon on board.) When Flip-Flop saw Moon winking at him, he jumped off his pole and flipped it over his shoulder. He put a little surprise package in his pocket and ran all the way to the farmhouse to get the children.

Kevin and Andrea were waiting for him. They climbed onto Flip-Flop's pole, strapped the picnic basket on tight, and waved good-bye to their Mom and Dad and Freckles the cat. *"Check your seat belts and hang on tight,"* called Mom. (Put Flip-Flop and children on board.) Off they flew – over the fields, higher than the trees, towards Moon. The children kept looking down at their farm, but soon they were too high in the sky to even see their home.

(Put stars and clouds on board.) Now they saw millions of flickering stars, soft clouds, and Moon. On and on – closer and closer and closer to Moon. Soon it was in full sight. Flip-Flop reminded Andrea and Kevin to hold on to the pole when they landed.

Moon was glad to see them. (Put picnic basket near moon.) *"We brought the picnic,"* yelled the children, *"but can we play first?"* "Of course," said Moon. *"You and Flip-Flop go off. Do you remember some of the moon games we played last time you visited?"* *"Oh yes,"* yelled Andrea as they ran off.

"Let's play Crater Leap," yelled Kevin. *"That is so much fun!"* Kevin, Andrea and Flip-Flop each found a big crater. Flip-Flop shouted out, *"Go!"* They began chasing each other as they leapt from crater to crater. Sometimes the craters were so wide they could hardly leap over them and other times the craters were so narrow, baby leaps were enough.

As they played, Flip-Flop kept checking his pocket to make sure the surprise package was still safe.

They were almost back to the picnic site when Flash Star came streaking down to see them. *"I thought I saw you visiting Moon. How about coming for a ride? I'll get two of my friends."* (Put children/Flip-Flop riding stars on board.) Kevin, Andrea, and Flip-Flop each climbed on a star and streaked off.

As they flew through the sky they joined some stars playing tag. After awhile Twinkle Star flew over and asked Kevin and Andrea, *"Would you like to send a message to your Mom and Dad?"* *"Oh yes. Tell them we love them and will be home in the morning,"* said Kevin. Twinkle and all her friends held hands and formed a giant heart in the sky. All together they flashed their bright lights. The flash landed right on the big window ledge of the farmhouse. Mom and Dad smiled as they looked out the window. They felt the love and knew everyone was having a good time on the moon.

"Let's race back to the picnic," said Flip-Flop. Moon was glad to see them and said, *"I bet you're hungry."* *"We sure are,"* said Flip-Flop. *"Well everything is ready. I set the table, poured our drinks, and spread out the food your mom made for us."* Moon looked at the 3 stars and said, *"Join us Stars. You must be hungry too."* So the Stars, Moon, Andrea, Kevin and Flip-Flop all sat down to eat. (What do you think they ate?)

(Put sun on board.) Soon Moon said, *"I must be going. It's time for Sun to rise."* Andrea, Kevin, and Flip-Flop had to go too. (Put surprise bag on moon.) Before they took off, Flip-Flop reached into his pocket and pulled out his surprise package and gave it to Moon. He said, *"Moon, here is a little present from my cornfield!"* Moon opened the gift. *"Thank you, Flip-Flop. You know how much I love popcorn!* (Put bowl of popcorn on board.) *I will pop these kernels in one of my craters, and then eat the popcorn with all my friends."*

(Put friends waving good-bye on board.) Everyone waved as the visitors flew off.

DIRECTIONS

Read the story. As you do put the felt pieces on the board.

TALK ABOUT THE STORY

"What do you think it would be like to fly through space? Would you like to ride with Flip-Flop on his pole?"

"If you were going to take a special present to MOON, what do you think you would take? Why?"

STORY GAMES

Stars: Put "glow-in-the-dark" stars on your ceiling. Turn off the lights and lie on the floor. Pretend you're taking a trip to the MOON. Have fun!!

Popcorn Snack: Make popcorn with your children. Pretend you are on the moon as you eat your special snack.

Make FELT PIECES

Flip-Flop and children on the pole
Surprise bag
Several stars
Moon
Several clouds
Flip-Flop on a star
Andrea on a star
Kevin on a star
Picnic basket
Sun
Bowl of popcorn
Flip-Flop and children on the pole waving good-bye

PICNIC ON THE MOON

PICNIC ON THE MOON

PICNIC ON THE MOON

PICNIC ON THE MOON

FLUFFY CLOUD

(Put FLUFFY CLOUD on board.) Hi! I'm FLUFFY CLOUD. I'm so glad that you're going to float along with me to visit some of my friends in the sky. As we go be sure to look for other clouds. You'll see some that are bigger and fluffier than I am and others that are smaller. Be sure to wave as we pass them.

OK now we're about ready to fly, so lie down on your back, put your hands under your head and relax. (Lie down.) We're off, floating up and up and up. Look! We're passing under some big clouds. Remember to wave. (Do it.)

We're getting close to my first friend. I'll give you some hints so you can begin to think about who she is. My friend flies in the sky, but lives on the earth. Sometimes she perches in trees and sometimes she walks on the ground. I see her now! She's flying right towards us. Shh! Let's not scare her. Quietly sit up and see if you can spot her. (Use your hands to make binoculars and look around.) Who do you think she is? (Put bird on board and quietly call out her name.) You're right, my first friend today is MRS. BIRD. Let's wave to her. (Do it.) Look, she's waving her wing back at us.

MRS. BIRD is flying closer to us. I wonder what she wants. I'm going to stop and listen to her. Guess what! MRS. BIRD wants to ride along with us. She also wants to bring her friend.

Let's see if we can guess who her friend is. MRS. BIRD says her friend is very, very small. She has red skin and lots of tiny black dots. She likes to fly around and land on people's arms, hands, and sometimes even their cheeks. It is said, that when she lands on you, she brings you good luck. Guess who MRS. BIRD brought with her. (Guess and put ladybug on board.) Yes, MRS. BIRD brought LADYBUG. Welcome aboard, LADYBUG. I'm glad you and MRS. BIRD are going to ride along with us.

Everyone lie down. We're off to visit another friend who flies very high in the sky. Feel the breeze as we go up and up. Up past more clouds. Are you ready for your clues? OK. Close your eyes and think. This friend is made of metal. Like the MRS. BIRD, this friend has wings. People use my friend a lot. They get inside of him and he  takes them on trips, just like I'm taking you on a trip. He's going to fly over us pretty soon. Quietly sit up. Get your binoculars ready and look up high. Can you see him? What is it? (Have the children call out what it is and put the airplane on the board.) You guessed my friend. It is an AIRPLANE. Look! The people on the plane are waving at us. Let's wave to them with both of our hands. (Do it.) Be careful. I don't want any of you falling off.

We are very high in the sky. Lie back down. I think it's time to start slowly drifting home. I'm going to look around as we go back. Maybe several more of my friends will be flying in the sky. You just relax and listen to the sounds and feel the warm sun.

Oh my. There's a friend I have not seen in several weeks. This friend is flying over the park where many of you play. Sit up, get your binoculars and see if you can spot him. He is a huge balloon with a basket attached to the bottom. See the red, blue, and yellow strips on his balloon. There are 4 people standing in the basket. They just saw us and are waving. Do you know what my friend's name is? (Talk about it.) It's called a HOT AIR BALLOON. (Put hot air balloon on board.)

We're almost back. I think I see one more friend. She is very colorful. She has a long string with colorful bows hanging from her. If I look carefully, I see a dad and a little girl holding onto the other end of the string. Quietly sit up and look. I don't think you'll need your binoculars. She is very close. Do you know what it is? (Softly call out what this friend is and put kite on board.) Yes, my friend is a KITE. Look, she's waving in the wind. Wave back at her.

We're about to land. Hold on, sometimes it's a little bumpy. (Land.) Thanks for coming with me today. Watch yourself as you climb off. I don't want any of you to get hurt. Please come back again. We'll go for another ride and look for more friends in the sky.

DIRECTIONS

Fold up a big bed sheet. As you read the first 2 sentences, *"Hi! I'm FLUFFY CLOUD"* unfold the sheet. Pretend that it is FLUFFY CLOUD. Sit on it as you continue to read this Riddle Story in a soft, quiet voice.

Put FLUFFY CLOUD on the felt board. Add the other clouds as you float under them. Continue adding felt pieces as you find each of FLUFFY CLOUD's friends in the sky.

TALK ABOUT THE STORY

"How do you think it feels to ride on a cloud?"

"If you could take a real ride on a cloud, would you? Why? Where would you like to go? What do you think you would see?"

"Who are your favorite friends on the sky?"

STORY GAMES!

More FLUFFY CLOUD ADVENTURES

1. Extend or change the story.

2. Take a whole new adventure and see several more of FLUFFY CLOUD's friends in the sky:

   - Animal Ride
     Owl
     Butterfly
     Hawk
     Duck
     Bat
   - Bug Ride
     Firefly
     Bee
     Mosquito
     Ladybug
     Fly

   - Night Ride
     Lightning
     Star
     Planet
     Comet
     Moon

Make FELT PIECES

Large FLUFFY CLOUD and
   several other smaller ones
   (Cut from white felt.)
Bird
Ladybug
Airplane
Hot air balloon
Kite

FLUFFY CLOUD

ZOO SAFARI

It was a bright, cool morning and our family decided to go to the zoo. We quickly packed a picnic lunch and we were off for the day. We arrived at the gate just as the zoo was opening. As we walked in, there were several black and white striped animals running around in a field. What were the first animals we saw? (ZEBRA.)

Our family continued walking along the path. Soon we came to an animal that had a long gray trunk and a huge body. What do you think we saw? (ELEPHANT.) We stood watching the elephant for awhile. We would have liked to throw him some peanuts, but there was a sign that said, DO NOT FEED THE ANIMALS.

We continued along, watching many of the animals romping around. After awhile we came to one of my very favorite animals. He had a very long neck, was yellow, and was covered with large brown spots. (GIRAFFE.) We stood there for awhile watching the

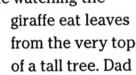

giraffe eat leaves from the very top of a tall tree. Dad said, *"Let's be on our way. There are lots more animals to enjoy."*

He was right! The very next ones we saw made us laugh all the while we watched them. These animals played on trapezes, swung from branches, tires, and ropes and jumped from tree to tree. They were? (MONKEYS.) As with many of the other animals, we could have enjoyed the monkeys all day; however, it was getting close to lunch time.

We sat on the picnic bench and ate. While we ate, a big bird strutted around the picnic area. He had a huge fan of colorful feathers. I didn't know what type of bird he was. Do you? (PEACOCK.) My mom told me it was a peacock. Other birds were flying overhead and landing in the trees all around the picnic tables. Well, lunch was over. We cleaned up and continued our ZOO SAFARI.

First we saw a huge, brown furry animal. He lumbered around the rocks and grass. Then he looked right at me and stood up on his hind legs. He was so tall. I think he was showing off. It was so exciting to see this animal. What was it? (BEAR.)

Next to the large bears were the lions, tigers, and leopards. It was getting late so Mom and Dad said we needed to start walking towards the car. On the way we saw another huge animal. He was lying in the mud to keep cool. While we were watching, he opened his gigantic mouth. Everyone

could see his teeth. They were the biggest ones I've ever seen. Do you think he goes to the dentist? Can you guess what animal this was? It's really a hard to say his name. (HIPPOPOTAMUS.)

The sun was setting and now we were all very tired. We agreed that it was time to go home. We stopped to have a drink of water and then went to the car. The next thing I remember was Mom and Dad carrying my brother and me into the house.

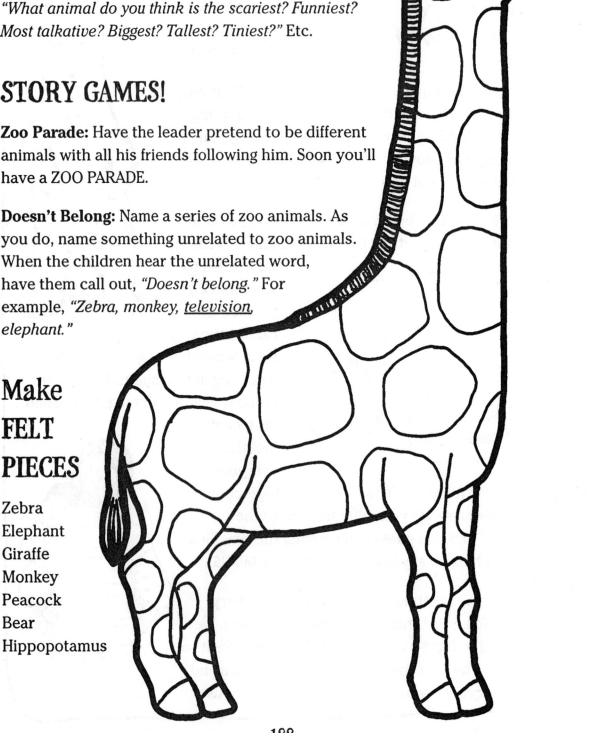

DIRECTIONS

Put the zoo animals on the felt board as you answer each riddle.

TALK ABOUT THE STORY

"Let's name all the animals we see at the zoo."

"What animal do you think is the scariest? Funniest? Most talkative? Biggest? Tallest? Tiniest?" Etc.

STORY GAMES!

Zoo Parade: Have the leader pretend to be different animals with all his friends following him. Soon you'll have a ZOO PARADE.

Doesn't Belong: Name a series of zoo animals. As you do, name something unrelated to zoo animals. When the children hear the unrelated word, have them call out, *"Doesn't belong."* For example, *"Zebra, monkey, television, elephant."*

Make FELT PIECES

Zebra
Elephant
Giraffe
Monkey
Peacock
Bear
Hippopotamus

ZOO SAFARI

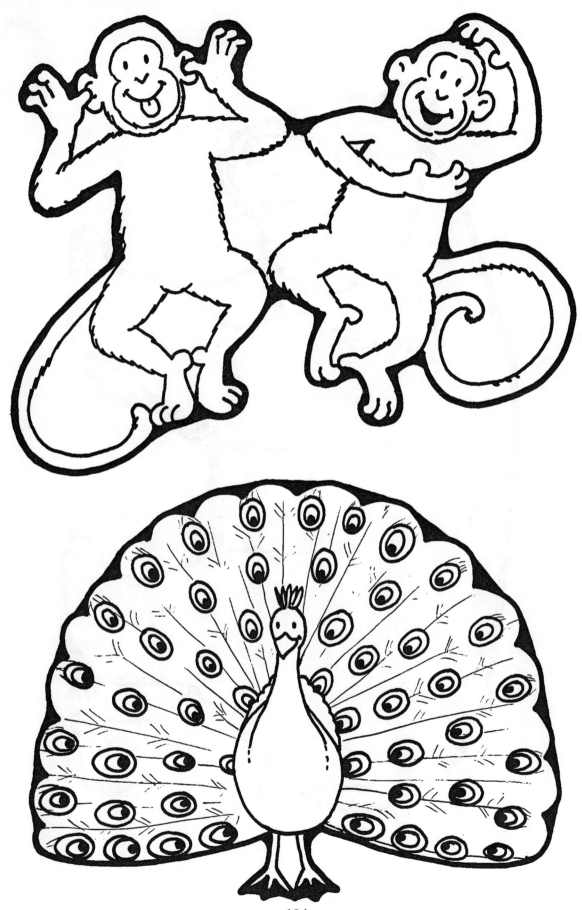

ZOO SAFARI

AFLOAT IN A BOAT

by Dick Wilmes

Afloat in a boat
Four friends and me.
The boat was rocking
On the deep blue sea.

One friend saw a **whale**
And leaning out wide.
Reached too far and
Fell over the side.

Afloat in a boat
Three friends and me.
The boat was rocking
On the deep blue sea.

One friend saw a **sea gull**
And stood up tall.
The boat started wiggling
And my friend did fall.

Afloat in a boat
Two friends and me.
The boat was rocking
On the deep blue sea.

One friend saw a **seal**
Just a resting on a rock.
Turned around to show us
And fell in. What a shock!

Afloat in a boat
One friend and me.
The boat was rocking
On the deep blue sea.

He saw an **octopus**
All slimy and green.
And fell in the water
Never more to be seen.

Afloat in a boat
Just little old me.
The boat was rocking
On the deep blue sea.

I saw a **shark**
And jumped with fright.
That shark ate me up
In just one bite!!

GULP!!

DIRECTIONS

Have the children hold up five fingers. Say AFLOAT IN A BOAT together. As each child in the Number Story falls into the "deep blue sea," lower one finger. As you say the last line of the story, have each child grab her fist with her other hand as if the shark is eating it.

At the beginning of verses 2, 4, 6, 8, and 10, put the appropriate felt animal on the board.

TALK ABOUT THE STORY

"Have you ever been in a boat? What were you doing? Fishing? Riding? Eating? Swimming?"

Talk about water safety.

- Always swim with an adult.
- Always wear a life preserver.
- Don't stand up in a boat.
- Swim close to shore.
- Swim in safe water.
- What else?

STORY GAMES!

Float the Boat: Put several small boats, people and cargo in a big tub of water. Let the children play.

Row, Row, Row Your Boat: Get a partner. Sit on the floor with your legs outstretched. Hold hands. Sing ROW, ROW, ROW YOUR BOAT as you rock back and forth.

Make FELT PIECES

Whale
Seagull
Seal
Octopus
Shark

AFLOAT IN A BOAT

AFLOAT IN A BOAT

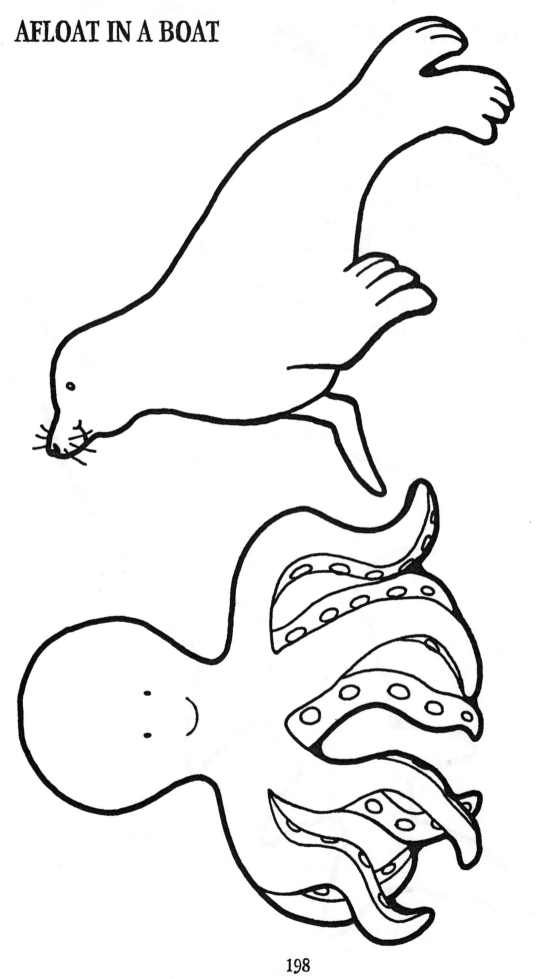

AFLOAT IN A BOAT

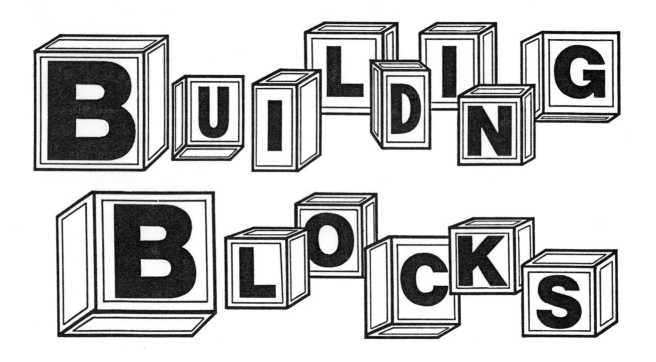

BUILDING BLOCKS Library

The Circle Time Series

by Liz and Dick Wilmes. Thousands of activities for large and small groups of children. Each book is filled with Language and Active games, Fingerplays, Songs, Stories, Snacks, and more. A great resource for every library shelf.

Circle Time Book
Captures the spirit of 39 holidays and seasons.
ISBN 0-943452-00-7   **$ 12.95**

Everyday Circle Times
Over 900 ideas. Choose from 48 topics divided into 7 sections: self-concept, basic concepts, animals, foods, science, occupations, and recreation.
ISBN 0-943452-01-5   **$16.95**

More Everyday Circle Times
Divided into the same 7 sections as EVERYDAY. Features new topics such as Birds and Pizza, plus all new ideas for some popular topics contained in EVERYDAY.
ISBN 0-943452-14-7   **$16.95**

Yearful of Circle Times
52 different topics to use weekly, by seasons, or mixed throughout the year. New Friends, Signs of Fall, Snowfolk Fun, and much more.
ISBN 0-943452-10-4   **$16.95**

CIRCLE TIME

Paint Without Brushes

by Liz and Dick Wilmes. Use common materials which you already have. Discover the painting possibilities in your classroom! PAINT WITHOUT BRUSHES gives your children open-ended art activities to explore paint in lots of creative ways. A valuable art resource. One you'll want to use daily.
ISBN 0-943452-15-5   **$12.95**

Easel Art

by Liz & Dick Wilmes. Let the children use easels, walls, outside fences, clip boards, and more as they enjoy the variety of art activities filling the pages of EASEL ART. A great book to expand young children's art experiences.
ISBN 0-943452-25-2   **$ 12.95**

Everyday Bulletin Boards

by Wilmes and Moehling. Features borders, murals, backgrounds, and other open-ended art to display on your bulletin boards. Plus board ideas with patterns, which teachers can make and use to enhance their curriculum.
ISBN 0-943452-09-0   **$ 12.95**

Exploring Art

by Liz and Dick Wilmes. EXPLORING ART is divided by months. Over 250 art ideas for paint, chalk, doughs, scissors, and more. Easy to set-up in your classroom.
ISBN 0-943452-05-8   **$19.95**

ART

Magnet Board Fun

by Liz and Dick Wilmes. Every classroom has a magnet board, every home a refrigerator. MAGNET BOARD FUN is crammed full of games, songs, and stories. Hundreds of patterns to reproduce, color, and use immediately.

ISBN 0-943452-28-7   **$ 16.95**

Parachute Play, Revised

by Liz and Dick Wilmes. Play, wiggle, and laugh as you introduce children to the parachute. Over 150 holiday and everyday games for inside and outside play.

ISBN 0-943452-30-9   **$ 12.95**

Activities Unlimited

by Adler, Caton, and Cleveland. Hundreds of innovative activities to develop fine and gross motor skills, increase language, become self-reliant, and play cooperatively. This book will quickly become a favorite.

ISBN 0-943452-17-1   **$16.95**

Felt Board Fingerplays

by Liz and Dick Wilmes. A year full of fingerplay fun. Over 50 popular fingerplays, with full-size patterns. All accompanied by games and activities.

ISBN 0-943452-26-0   **$16.95**

Felt Board Fun

by Liz and Dick Wilmes. Make your felt board come alive. This unique book has over 150 ideas with patterns.

ISBN 0-943452-02-3   **$16.95**

Felt Board Stories

by Liz and Dick Wilmes. 25 seasonal, holiday, and any-day stories with full-size patterns. Children are involved in each story. They figure out riddles, create endings, sing with characters, add patterns, and so much more.

ISBN 0-943452-31-7   **$16.95**

Table & Floor Games

by Liz and Dick Wilmes. 32 easy-to-make, fun-to-play table/floor games with accompanying patterns ready to duplicate. Teach beginning concepts such as matching, counting, colors, alphabet, and so on.

ISBN 0-943452-16-3   **$19.95**

Learning Centers

by Liz and Dick Wilmes. Hundreds of open-ended activities to quickly involve and excite your children. You'll use it every time you plan and whenever you need a quick, additional activity. A must for every teacher's bookshelf.

ISBN 0-943452-13-9   **$19.95**

Play With Big Boxes

by Liz and Dick Wilmes. Children love big boxes. Turn them into boats, telephone booths, tents, and other play areas. Bring them to art and let children collage, build, and paint them. Use them in learning centers for games, play stages, quiet spaces, puzzles, and more, more, more.

ISBN 0-943452-23-6   **$ 12.95**

Play With Small Boxes

by Liz and Dick Wilmes. Small boxes are free, fun, and unlimited. Use them for telephones, skates, scoops, pails, doll beds, buggies, and more. So many easy activities, you'll use small boxes every day.

ISBN 0-943452-24-4   **$ 12.95**

Games for All Seasons

by Caton and Cleveland. Play with the wonder of seasons and holidays. Use acorns, pumpkins, be clouds and butterflies, go ice fishing. Over 150 learning games.

ISBN 0-943452-29-5   **$16.95**

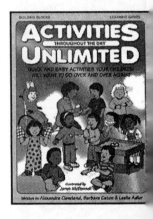

On Track To KINDERGARTEN

by Alex Cleveland
and Barb Caton.

Parents always ask: *"How can I help my child get ready for kindergarten?"* This book is the answer. The weekly activity sheets are filled with games and activities for parents to do with their children.

Available in Spanish and English.

ISBN 0-943452-32-5 (English) $14.95

ISBN 0-943452-33-3 (Spanish) $14.95

2's Experience Series

by Liz and Dick Wilmes. An exciting series developed especially for toddlers and twos!

-Art
ble, Paint, Smear, Mix , , Mold, Taste, and more. r 150 activities, plus lots cipes and hints.
0-943452-21-X $16.95

2's-Sensory Play
Hundreds of playful, multi-sensory activities to encourage children to look, listen, taste, touch, and smell.
ISBN 0-943452-22-8 $14.95

2's-Dramatic Play
Dress up and pretend! Hundreds of imaginary situations and settings.

ISBN 0-943452-20-1 $12.95

Stories
te children with story s! Read—Expand the es with games, songs, rhymes. Over 40 books patterns.
0-943452-27-9 $16.95

2's-Fingerplays
A wonderful collection of easy fingerplays with accompanying games and large FINGERPLAY CARDS.

ISBN 0-943452-18-X $12.95

2's-Felt Board Fun
Make your felt board come alive. Enjoy stories, activities, and rhymes. Hundreds of extra large patterns.

ISBN 0-943452-19-8 $14.95

BUILDING BLOCKS

BUILDING BLOCKS Subscription	$20.00

CIRCLE TIME Series
CIRCLE TIME BOOK	12.95
EVERYDAY CIRCLE TIMES	16.95
MORE EVERYDAY CIRCLE TIMES	16.95
YEARFUL OF CIRCLE TIMES	16.95

ART
EASEL ART	12.95
EVERYDAY BULLETIN BOARDS	12.95
EXPLORING ART	19.95
PAINT WITHOUT BRUSHES	12.95

LEARNING GAMES & ACTIVITIES
ACTIVITIES UNLIMITED	16.95
FELT BOARD FINGERPLAYS	16.95
FELT BOARD FUN	16.95
FELT BOARD STORIES	16.95
LEARNING CENTERS	19.95
MAGNET BOARD FUN	16.95
PARACHUTE PLAY, REVISED	12.95
PLAY WITH BIG BOXES	12.95
PLAY WITH SMALL BOXES	12.95
TABLE & FLOOR GAMES	19.95

ON TRACK TO KINDERGARTEN
ENGLISH EDITION	14.95
SPANISH EDITION	14.95

2's EXPERIENCE Series
2'S EXPERIENCE - ART	16.95
2'S EXPERIENCE - DRAMATIC PLAY	12.95
2'S EXPERIENCE - FELTBOARD FUN	14.95
2'S EXPERIENCE - FINGERPLAYS	12.95
2'S EXPERIENCE - SENSORY PLAY	14.95
2'S EXPERIENCE - STORIES	16.95

Prices subject to change without notice.

All books available from full-service book stores, educational stores, and school supply catalogs.

Check Our Website:
www.bblocksonline.com

QUALITY BUILDING BLOCKS SINCE 1977